# MEAI

GW01460193

## ALAN BURKE

GWAITHEL & GILWERN

# Contents

Published in 2001 by Gwaithel & Gilwern, Gladestry, Powys, HR5 3NT, Wales and printed by Printex, Kington, Herefordshire.

ISBN 0-9527558-15

## Introduction

In the summer of 1999 Alan Burke wrote asking if we could meet to talk about his poems. In his letter he mentioned that he was seriously ill. We were somewhat cautious, since it has to be said that poetry often attracts unhappy and damaged people who need a kind of help which poets can rarely supply. But we arranged a rendezvous.

Alan was a charming and highly intelligent young man, taking leave from studying Theology at Durham University to battle with his cancer. Within minutes of meeting him, he told us that his condition had spread to his brain and was now terminal. Equally prominent was the need to stake a claim on life, and on immortality, by means of his poems. His urgent sense of value of poetry was startling - a reminder of why we ourselves had begun to write it.

We planned further contact, but Alan's illness swiftly worsened, and he died at home in the West End of Newcastle in August 1999. Gerry Wardle had arranged the printing of a postcard of his poem 'A Young Person Talks About Dying', so Alan knew he was in print before he died. The Newcastle Journal also ran the poem.

We wanted to print a small selection of Alan's work as a tribute to him and his family. It's very difficult to talk critically about the work of a writer who died so young and in the middle of his apprenticeship to poetry. It would be wrong to make large claims for the work he produced. But it is full of startling phrases and ideas and lit by a humbling candour and courage, and by a passion for writing and for experience - all of which suggests that Alan was the real thing. So this little book is for him and his family.

Sean O'Brien and Jo Shapcott

## Instants Terrain

Look out across the Instants terrain
View the world from that higher plain,
Take its sky in your hands
Count the grains of the stretching sands
Show that you master your own lands.
Then stride through the conquered day
Flicking mountains out the way
Urge to come All that may
Good or bad, gold or grey.

## Railway Boy

Knotted to his father's ropey
Arm, the lad is
Tied to his life so tight it's
Choking!
Though a tumour or a car-bonnet
Ten years hence has his Death's
Name ingrained on to it,
This second is his
Rich sea to sail on in
Which ever ramshackle
Pile he puts in the water.

By the time they come to
Their counter,
He's already forgotten his
Previous ten minute
Long wait-journey -
He's reached the Bermudas
From the Cape of Good Hope

With out so much as being
Splashed by a drop of water.
But he does hold aloft,
Over his freckled face,
The winners golden plate
For ten whole, long minutes
Pounded out from
Its ore into His journey.

After receiving
Reservation tickets,
They shuffle out into their
Future -
A spread-eagle Goddess,
Ready for them both to
Enter.

I follow their lives out the door
With my rapacious eyes,
Get my ticket
And skulk off.

## Fruit Man

A bowl of strawberries
All my hearts
Red beating and sweet
Pouring out cream
They taste *so* good.
Why haven't I sunk my teeth
Into them before?

I peel a banana,
Pulling back my wrist-skin.
I take a bite
Only to get a mouthful of
Bone and veins.

This orange,
My eye,
With which I see the strawberries
And banana
Is the tomb for a pip -
My cataract forbidding
Me to see properly.

## The Cancer Slide

Pinned down by Fascinations'
Burly hands,
Struggle slapped out of me -
"Open wide's" the command
As a litre of liquidised Question
Is poured down my throat
Drowning my breath like a drunken sailor.
I capitulate.

My Veronicaless via Dolarosa
To the lab.
With a 400 pound chunk
Of Intrigue
Balanced parrot fashion
On my shoulder,
Whipped by draught
As I push by
Mobs of healers, lepers
And the possessed.
Climbing the stairs -

There it is . . .
Hitting the landscape of my
Eyes like a meteor
  'Oncolab'

From a smoking tub a
Rack is removed and
Laid in front of me . . .
I retch up a mouthful of pungent
Fear
Splattering all over the
Surgeon's typed green file.
And the rack.

Wiping the specks of my
Fear off his face,
The surgeon pull out a slide
Buttered with the
Me gone mad,
The
Self destroying self.

I was hoping to see
Snarling minute cannibals,
Gobs crammed with me,
Frozen in action inside
Their transparent mausoleum,

Instead,
Sorrow
Ninja-like, infiltrates my
Brain unseen.

Big blobs amongst many
Smaller blobs,
Reminding me of a child
I once spotted leaving
Nursery . . . 10 feet she must've
Been - a bo'na fi'de freak,
Taunted by her class I imagine.
Like wise, these cells' efforts
At blending in
Failed
The jeers and whispers drove them
Insane . .
(I wonder if that girl does
A Charles Whitman special one day?)

The surgeon speaks,
An empty voice jam packed with words
"You're LUCKY . . . eighty percent . . tumour . . dead" -
That means twenty percent of
Them
Were still alive on being removed
Damn! They put the Auschwitz
Nazis to shame,
Butchering butchering up to the
Last possible moment as
Chemo. banged on their
Destructions' door.

They would have . . . ki . . . killed, me.

Their fundamental
me-less-ness
Shocks my empathy
Out of its skin.
My memory's eyes fill with
Tears
At what they put me through.

## Meal for One

How I need to love
But I'm just too scared,
Therefore let me die
And I'll court Angels instead.

My heart sniggers at me continually
And screams as I try to sleep -
How I'd love to silence it
By falling in love, deep.

A meal for one I buy
And at table stiffly sit,
silence howls all round
In the cafe dimly lit.

The world processses me rapidly
As I give it a little smile,
Much too busy it is
To talk with me a while.

My spirit begs a partner
My heart leaves after a row
I don't care about such things,
I get used to everything now.

## A Rose Sequence

i

The rose
Is nature's imitation of an
Angel -
Those who, millions of years ago
Implored God to show
Mercy on blandness.
Thus came about the
Created uncreatable -
The rose.

ii

The rose,
Hero worshipped by the little daisy,
The bane of the weed
Beautifier of grass
A stud to the lady flowers!
And the super-model of plants!
The rose.

iii

The rose
I see from my window
Has blossomed
Beauty into a divinity,
Has become an
Intense aberration of
Orthodox colour
Outshining the noon light
To a humiliated
Pitch black
The rose.

iv

The rose
Which there
Wilts in a florist's bucket
And one freely danced to the
Sun's song
Will probably be bought by
An adulterous spouse or
Become one of the
Lovers' tools to crack
The rock of an un-receptive heart!
But soon its beauty will
Drop off in tears,
And in the bin will go
The rose.

**A Young Person on dying**

Though Life cared to play with me so very short a time,
True Life comes in Death, so my Death is no great crime.
Instead I'll play with Immortality - he's always up for fun
And we'll sit and laugh at Death - that funniest of puns.
For everywhere I ever was, there I'll always be,
But you'll have to drop your human eyes if you want to gaze
    on me.
For I'll be your deepest comfort during your deepest pain.
But look out into the universe shortly after I die
And concentrate intently on any twinkle in the sky.
I'll be bungee jumping off Pluto, zooming around the sun,
Piggy-backing angles. Yes! Death's a prize hard won.

Alan Burke died in 1999 aged twenty while he was a student of theology at Durham University. He left behind a large collection of astonishingly vibrant poems. The poets Sean O'Brien and Jo Shapcott have chosen a selection of his work to publish here, in this small book, as a tribute to his talent and promise.

ISBN 0 9527558-15

JUNE 1984.

GW01459954

# ATHENS

**By the staff of Editions Berlitz**

**Revised edition 1981**

# Preface

A new kind of travel guide for the jet age. Berlitz has packed all you need to know about Athens into this compact and colourful book, one of an extensive series on the world's top tourist areas.

Like our phrase books and dictionaries, this book fits your pocket—in both size and price. It also aims to fit your travel needs.

- It concentrates on your specific destination—Athens—not an entire country.

- It combines easy reading with fast facts: what to see and do, where to shop, what to eat.

- An authoritative A-to-Z "blueprint" at the end of the book gives clear-cut answers to all your questions—from "Where can I send a telegram?" to "How do I get from the airport to town?" plus how to get there, when to go and what to budget for.

- Easy-to-read-maps in full colour pinpoint sights you'll want to see.

In short, this handy guide will help you enjoy your visit to Athens. From the Pláka with its picturesque, winding streets to the wonders of the National Archaeological Museum, from an excursion to Delphi to the pulsating sound of the *bouzoúki*, Berlitz tells you clearly and concisely what it's all about.

Let your travel agent help you choose a hotel.
Let a restaurant guide help you find a good place to eat.
But to decide "What should we do today?" travel with Berlitz.

Photography: Geraldine Kenway and Daniel Vittet.
We're grateful to Don Larrimore, Vicky Nicolopoulou and Hilary Louise Turner and to the National Tourist Organization of Greece for their valuable assistance.

 Cartography: Falk-Verlag, Hamburg.

# Contents

*Maps:* Athens p. 25, Ancient Athens p. 39, Modern Athens pp. 54–55, Excursions p. 67
*Cover:* The Parthenon

### How to use this guide
If time is short, look for items to visit which are printed in bold type in this book, e.g. **Agía Ekateríni.** Those sights most highly recommended are not only given in bold type but also carry our traveller symbol, e.g. **the Parthenon.**

# Athens and the Athenians

Sparkling there in the Aegean sun, its marble marvels proudly proclaim that this city was the glory of the classical world. For every visitor, Athens holds an undeniable fascination—so many centuries spanned, so much of Western civilization rooted here.

The city centre, just 4 miles from the sea, is scanned by a gentle audience of hills. Crowning Athens—as it has since the dawn of Greek history—the Acropolis with its breathtaking Parthenon.

Considering the very real ravages of man and time, the wonder is that any of the city's venerable monuments have survived. Yet the ancients would hardly recognize Athens today. Europe's southernmost capital is experiencing acute growing pains. Suburbs of cement and steel sprawl

*Modern Athens sprawls out at the foot of Mount Likavittós; the city's young people are not so different from their counterparts elsewhere.*

chaotically over its historic basin, and the crystal-like quality of Attica's light, famous since Homer, has become little more than a memory. Swollen by unrelenting floods of Greeks migrating from the countryside, Athens' population has soared to some 3 million. The entire country contains only 9 million people.

Despite the congestion, this city will inevitably delight. Life is an outdoor extravaganza, a blend of classical and cosmopolitan. Parks, squares, even roof gardens are cluttered with statuary. Where Aristotle and Plato strolled in togas pondering the universe, tycoons behind sun glasses close multi-million-drachma shipping deals. Or that's what they seem to be doing over little cups of coffee under café awnings.

Bulging sponge sellers amble past, shoeshine boys snap their rags. On the broad, tree-lined boulevards sports cars and air-conditioned tour buses wheel past the ancient ruins. Near a Doric column, smoke rises from charcoal embers, the intoxicating odour of broiling meat permeating the air. A svelte Kolonáki matron chats on an outdoor phone, oblivious to the exotic Byzantine church rising in front of her; a banker waits in line to buy pistachio nuts from the corner vendor. With worry beads clicking everywhere, smiles far outnumber frowns.

Making up this urban agglomeration are all manner of villages. Each quarter has its *platía,* its local shops. Try any *kafenion* for a Turkish coffee and the ever-present tumbler of cold water. You'll soon meet the neighbourhood philosophers. Your coffee, *oúzo* or *tsái* (tea) entitles you to a table for the day. But a better way to sample the kaleidoscopic texture of Athens is to stroll—morning or evening.

During the white-hot afternoon hours, the city's bustle dies away, the streets are shuttered. Athens drowses in ritual observance of that most logical of Mediterranean traditions, the siesta—just as it doubtless did under Pericles.

When the sun starts its downward curve, the pace picks up again. Offices and boutiques reopen, often until 8.30 p.m. Shopping streets throb with activity, cafés fill up, neon blinks on, the first strains of *bouzoúki* music are heard from the labyrinth of *tavérnes* beneath the Acropolis.

Since earliest times, Athens has been a world crossroads.

**8**

Lines etched in some deeply-tanned faces betray lifetimes at sea or in the mountains. Generally Athenians are short in stature and dark-haired. Some could pass as replicas of their discus-throwing ancestors who pose classically in the museums.

These are volatile, talkative, irrepressibly curious people. They pamper their babies and

*Black-robed and bearded, Orthodox priests are an integral part of life.*

honour their grandparents. Their pride is quiet and dignified. You'll see men walking arm in arm arguing passionately, a favourite pastime.

The Athenians' surpassing kindness to foreigners reflects the tradition of generous hospitality instinctive to all Greeks. At the same time you'll come to respect the local business acumen, whether you're buying a flea-market trinket or trying to charter a yacht.

In and near Athens there's enough to see and do to make any holiday seem too short. With the formidable heat through the summer months, you'll want to avoid any thought of rushing. If the urban din starts to fray nerves, beaches and get-away islands are readily accessible. Or seek out a mountain-top or monastery in the Attic hills surrounding the capital.

Athens, a city very much on the move, tends to absorb effortlessly its waves of visitors, while straining its Hellenic ingenuity for greater commercial and industrial prominence. Yet in the end, no matter how modern it becomes or how much "progress" it achieves, Athens cannot escape the splendid heritage its

very name evokes.

## It's Greek to Me

Finding your way around in Athens will be much easier if you learn the Greek alphabet. This isn't as difficult as it sounds! All street signs are written in capital letters—many of which are already familiar to you. See ALPHABET in the Blueprint section of this book for a quick course in reading Greek.

So that you can pronounce the Greek street names, we have given their transcriptions. In the case of well-known sites (like Athens, Corinth and Delphi) and proper names in a historical or literary context, we've used the time-honoured English spelling.

Stress, a very important feature of the Greek language, is indicated by an accent mark (´) over the vowel of the syllable to be emphasized.

Two words you'll want to learn immediately are ΠΛΑΤΕΙΑ *(platia)*, meaning square, and ΟΔΟΣ *(odós)*, street, which are often omitted in addresses.

*A young Greek beauty admirably completes a classical Aphrodite.*

# A Brief History

The origins of Athens go back some 5,000 years, a lineage so ancient as to make all other European cities seem young by comparison. The first settlers on the Acropolis were probably the Pelasgians. Little is really known about these primitive tribespeople, but we have reams of fanciful mythology.

The legendary history of Athens begins with a contest: Athena, goddess of wisdom, and Poseidon, god of the sea, both had their eye on the city. It was agreed that the one who came up with the more useful gift for mortals would win. The half-human, half-serpent king of Athens, Cecrops, served as arbiter. He found Athena's offering of an olive tree the more valuable, and she became the city's special protector.

Starting about 2000 B.C., wandering bands from western Russia or Asia Minor filtered into Attica and other parts of Greece. Known as Achaeans, they were the first Greek-speaking people. Over the centuries they developed the rich Mycenaean civilization centred in the Peloponnesus, erecting many imposing **11**

## Divine Dozen

Every Greek schoolchild can reel off the names and particulars of the family of 12 top deities on Mount Olympus:

**Zeus**—supreme ruler of the gods and men, protector of Greece, master of the weather; his symbols are the eagle and the oak tree.

**Hera**—Zeus's third and oft-betrayed wife, protectress of marriage, mothers and the home.

**Athena**—the daughter of Zeus, goddess of wisdom, guardian of war heroes, reputedly invented the flute and the potter's wheel.

**Apollo**—son of Zeus, god of the sun, music, healing and prophecy (his advice was sought at the oracle of Delphi).

**Artemis**—twin sister of Apollo, goddess of hunting and of the moon, guardian of women and cities.

**Hermes**—son of Zeus, messenger of the gods, the god of commerce, protector of flocks, thieves and travellers, inventor of racing, boxing and the lyre.

**Ares**—son of Zeus, god of war, unpopular on Olympus and feared by the Greeks.

**Hephaestus**—son of Zeus, god of fire and industry, the lame blacksmith of the gods who supplied Zeus with thunderbolts.

**Aphrodite**—the daughter of Zeus, goddess of love, beauty and gardens, the most beautiful goddess of Olympus.

**Poseidon**—Zeus's brother, god of seas, rivers, earthquakes and anger, caused storms with his trident, moved to an undersea Aegean palace when Zeus defeated him in a struggle for control of the sky.

**Hestia**—Zeus's elder sister, beloved goddess of fire and the hearth, protectress of the home, family and city.

**Demeter**—sister of Zeus, goddess of agriculture, protectress of crops, taught men to grow corn.

fortresses. In the minor Acropolis of Athens, a wall and palace were built.

The Achaeans' chief rivals, and mentors, were the dazzling Minoans of Crete—that is until about 1450 B.C. when their empire was devastated, perhaps by tidal waves from the eruption of the volcanic island of Thera. For the next several centuries, the Mycenaeans dominated the Aegean and eastern Mediterranean. But a long series of conflicts, including the legendary siege of Troy,

weakened these mighty mainland warriors.

About 1100 B.C. waves of Dorians swept into the area on horseback. With iron spears and shields they overwhelmed the Bronze Age chariots of Mycenae and broke down the Peloponnesian bastions. The ensuing "dark ages" lasted about three centuries.

Somehow, Athens escaped the scourge and, after 700 B.C., took over and carried to unimagined heights the heritage of Mycenae and Crete.

*Graceful red-figure pottery and a powerful Poseidon sculpted in a dramatic pose illustrate the consummate artistry of the Ancients.*

Though they warred as often as they united with each other, Athenians, Spartans, Thebans and the others shared a definite sense of identity. They were all Greeks; they had a common language and an evolving pan-Hellenic religion. In addition, the Olympic, Delphian and Isthmian games played an important role in bringing the diverse Greeks together at regular intervals for these ritual athletic contests.

Athens, the largest city-state, came to embrace the entire Attica peninsula. The legendary King Theseus, slayer of the minotaur in the Cretan labyrinth, was revered by later Athenians for bringing Attica's scattered independent villages under the rule of the Acropolis. Countless pots and jars were decorated with drawings of Theseus's heroic exploits, but he belongs to myth not history. In fact, the villages merged with Athens in exchange for protection, full citizenship rights and a share of state offices.

### From Aristocracy to Democracy

Long a monarchy in the shadowy era before the 7th century B.C., Athens emerged into history as an oligarchy. Certain clans seem to have had special claim on positions conferring power and privilege, such as judges, war-lords and priests.

But the rule of law was inexorably extended. Thus Draco, whose code of laws became a byword for severity, put an end to family blood-feuds around 620 B.C.

Athens' first great historical figure is Solon—general, merchant, poet and sage—who became chief magistrate in 594 B.C. The city-state was torn by struggle between "haves" and "have-nots" (ancient Greek expressions). Armed with near-absolute powers, Solon produced a constitution advancing the ideal of equality before the law for citizens of all classes. He set up a trial-by-jury system, emancipated the peasantry from debt to land-owners and introduced far-reaching reforms which revived a languishing economy.

In the middle of the 6th century, the first dictator took power in Athens. This was Pisistratus. He set up a dynasty which continued, with interruptions, for half a century. (Forced out on one occasion, he dressed a tall, beautiful country girl to look like Athena, then entered Athens in triumph with the "goddess"

National Tourist Office of Greece

leading a procession.) A resourceful tyrant, Pisistratus put Athens on course toward greatness in commerce and the arts. Attica's wine and olive oil were shipped to Italy, Egypt and Asia Minor in beautiful black-figure pots; the standard version of Homer, Greece's first and greatest poet, was set down; the first tragedies in theatrical history

*Making the most of ruins – a modern performance in an old setting.*

were performed at the annual festival of the wine god, Dionysus.

The Pisistratus dynasty lost power in 508 B.C., and Cleisthenes, the true founder of Athenian democracy, took over. An aristocrat by birth, he was a radical by force of circumstance if not personal conviction. Cleisthenes invented electoral wards called *demes* and set up a sovereign citizens' assembly and a senate whose members were chosen by lot. He also introduced the inspired system of "ostracism"—any citizen becoming dangerously too big for his boots could be banished from Athens for ten years, but without loss of property.

## Persian Wars

Greece now entered the period of the Persian Wars. The Persians' far-flung dominions included Greek settlements on the coast of present-day Turkey. When the Greek towns attempted a revolt in 499 B.C., Athens helped them. Angered at this impudence, King Darius decided it was time to incorporate the Greek mainland and islands in his empire. In 490 B.C. he confidently launched an invasion of Attica. His forces and resources were vastly superior, but Darius hadn't reckoned with the amazing courage and battlefield skill of the Greeks.

On the plain of Marathon, some 10,000 Athenian infantry under General Miltiades inflicted a crippling, humiliating defeat on the Persians. (The soldier who ran 26 miles back to Athens died of exhaustion after reporting the victory.)

When Darius's son, Xerxes, re-invaded in far greater strength by land and sea ten years later, Greece seemed destined for defeat. But a few hundred heroic troops under Leonidas of Sparta held up the enormous Persian army at the pass of Thermopylae just long enough for Athens to be evacuated. Vowing to avenge his father's defeat, Xerxes swept in, seized and plundered the city, burning down all the wooden structures on the Acropolis.

He then climbed a hill to watch his fleet of 700 ships engage Themistocles' much smaller naval force in the Bay of Salamis. With brilliant tactics and newer ships, the Greek fleet managed to trounce the Persians. That crucial battle of 480 B.C. turned the tide. Soon thereafter, Xerxes' troops were soundly beaten at Plataea in the final, decisive battle of the

Persian Wars. Greek independence had been preserved and with it the foundations of Western civilization.

For almost 50 years, peace reigned at home and the victorious city-state knew its most magnificent era. Transforming a maritime league into an empire, Athens amassed money from her "subject allies" to build in perpetual marble the Parthenon and other monuments that adorn the Acropolis today.

The moving spirit behind this unprecedented time of greatness, the Golden Age, was Pericles. This liberal-inclined aristocrat was in effect the supreme ruler of Athens and its empire for 30 years, until his death in 429 B.C.

Innumerable works of art, literature, philosophy and science of great and enduring worth were produced by what Pericles called the "school of Hellas". The geniuses we see memorialized in Athens today as so many marble busts and street names were often close personal friends: the historian Herodotus and the tragic poet Sophocles, for example, and the brilliant scientists Zeno and Anaxagoras. The first literary salon in history was held by Aspasia, exotic mistress of Pericles.

## Classical Giants

**Ictinus** and **Callicrates:** architects of the Parthenon.

**Phidias:** sculptor of the Parthenon whose incomparable gold and ivory statues of Athena on the Acropolis and Zeus at Olympia (one of the seven wonders of the ancient world) have not survived.

**Aeschylus** (*The Persians*), **Sophocles** (*Oedipus Rex*) and **Euripides** (*The Trojan Women*): creators of Greek tragedy. **Aristophanes** (*The Wasps, The Birds*): creator of Greek comedy.

**Herodotus:** "Father of history" whose accounts of the conflict between Europe and Asia blended legend and fact.

**Thucydides:** author of the *History of the Peloponnesian War*, established an objective "science" of history.

**Socrates:** philosopher-orator condemned to drink the hemlock for "dangerous" questioning of fundamental beliefs.

**Plato** (*The Republic, Dialogues*): political and religious philosopher.

**Aristotle:** political, metaphysical and ethical philosopher, physicist, biologist, zoologist, tutor of Alexander the Great.

**Praxiteles:** sculptor of the Olympic *Hermes*.

*Greeks hope the new generation's life will be easier than theirs.*

course, the number of citizens (free adult males) was small —probably not above 30,000 —while the entire population including women, children, resident aliens and slaves was perhaps ten times as great.

Slavery was common, justified on the grounds that "democracy" could not exist unless the citizens were free to devote themselves to the service of the state. Most slaves in Athens were war prisoners.

## Peloponnesian War

As Athens prospered, intense economic and ideological rivalry developed with Greece's other powerful city-state, Sparta. In 431 B.C. the Peloponnesian War broke out between them. For 27 years the debilitating conflict dragged on, involving most of the Greek world. Finally Sparta, with naval help from former foe Persia, cut off Athens' vital corn supply by blockade and achieved complete victory. Yet within a few years —such was the vigour of this remarkable people—the Athenians had re-established a maritime alliance and recovered part of their Aegean empire.

Nonetheless, Athens' days as a great political power were over. As it and the other city-

During all this, the Athenian political system allowed an average *citizen* a greater degree of participation in public life than ever before anywhere, and perhaps since. Of

**18**

states became weaker by feuding among themselves, a new star rose in the north—that of Philip II of Macedon, father of Alexander the Great. Philip advanced the far-sighted scheme of a federation of Greek states, which Athens, swayed by the *Philippics* of master orator Demosthenes, resisted for a long period. But after losing the battle of Chaeronea in 338 B.C., the Athenians accepted an alliance and even sent Philip a gold crown as a token of submission.

Culturally and intellectually, Athens remained unsurpassed through the 4th century and thus the capital of Greek civilization. Aristotle, the towering thinker with one of history's most encyclopaedic minds, held forth at his Lyceum; Menander wrote comic plays; Praxiteles sculpted scores of superb statues, including the *Hermes* which he called "of no account" but which is probably the greatest extant Greek sculpture (on view in the museum at Olympia). This age in fact had even more lasting influence on Rome and Byzantium and through them on medieval and Renaissance Europe than Athens' great "classical" 5th century.

## Roman Rule

Macedonian troops occupied Athens twice, in 322 and 262 B.C., as the city continued to decline. Eventually, after a series of wars, the empire of Philip and Alexander was dismantled by the far-ranging legions of Rome. Macedonia became just another Roman province (146 B.C.) and Athens not much more than a showplace museum city. But it did have its philosophy schools and orators that attracted Romans with political ambitions. Cicero and Horace spent student years in Athens, and Emperor Hadrian is said to have been initiated into the sacred mysteries of Demeter at Eleusis.

Although generally treated well during some five centuries of Pax Romana, Athens suffered severely on one occasion. In 86 B.C., Roman general Sulla sacked the city in retribution for its unwise alliance with Mithridates, a Hellenized Persian and bitter enemy of Rome. Many Athenian treasures were carried off to Italy.

It was Athens' good fortune that some Romans were builders, not looters. Most notable was the Emperor Hadrian (A.D. 76–138), who loved classical Greek architecture. Among other things, he erect- **19** ed his distinctive arched gate and completed the temple of Olympian Zeus on foundations laid by Pisistratus nearly seven centuries earlier.

## Byzantine and Ottoman Obscurity

Roman Emperor Constantine gave Christianity official sanction; in 326 he chose as his "New Rome" the old Greek colonial town of Byzantium, dubbed Constantinople. Athens thereby lost all chance of becoming the chief city of the eastern Mediterranean. Under Byzantine rule the city of Pericles sank into deep provincial obscurity. Devastated once by rampaging Goths (A.D. 267), it otherwise merited only a few brief mentions in the history of the following centuries.

Christianity had taken early root in Greece, after a visit to Athens by St. Paul about A.D. 50. But the new religion didn't really put an end to the ancient polytheism until 529, when an edict by Emperor Justinian closed down the last "pagan" temples and the Athenian schools of philosophy.

In the 13th and 14th centuries, Athens was governed by a succession of adventurers from Burgundy, Catalonia and Florence.

Athens and Attica fell to the Turks in 1456, three years after these new empire-builders had taken Constantinople. For nearly four centuries of oppressive Ottoman rule—known as Greece's darkest age—Athens was all but forgotten. The Orthodox Church provided its people with their only sense of continuity with the past.

Venetians briefly took Athens away from the Turks in 1466 and again in 1687, when one of their shells hit a munitions store in the Parthenon, badly damaging the 2,000-year-old structure. Venice considered this no blemish on the illustrious career of the commander, Francesco Morosini, but art lovers do not honour his memory.

## Independence

Athens dwindled ever further. When the English poet Lord Byron visited it in 1809, he found that what had once been the glittering centre of the civilized world now numbered only about 5,000 souls.

Starting in 1821, it took 11 years and formidable foreign help for the Greeks to win their war of independence against the Turks. Athens and the Acropolis changed hands more than once during the long struggle in which many Englishmen, Scots, Irish and French fought with the Greeks. Byron, who popularized the cause abroad, died at Missolonghi in 1824.

*Bitter clashes caused deep suffering before the Turks were overthrown.*

The last Turks weren't evicted from the Acropolis until 1833. The following year, the little town of Athens became the capital of modern Greece. Theoretically sovereign, the new state was an artificial creation: the Great Powers had installed the young Bavarian Prince Otto

*Piraeus: after 2,000 years Greece is again a major maritime power.*

as king. He and his queen, Amalia, were deposed in 1862, but during this reign Athens slowly became a city again and Greece made considerable economic progress.

Complex European diplomatic bargaining then resulted in the establishment on the Greek throne in 1863 of another adolescent, 17-year-old William of the Danish royal house (Schleswig-Holstein-Sonderburg-Glücksburg). He took the name George I, King of the Hellenes, and reigned for 50 years until his assassination in 1913.

## The 20th Century

Greek history over the past eight decades has been as chaotic as any since the days of the ancients. The dominant figure between 1910 and 1935 was Eleftherios Venizelos, a

Cretan politician who was several times prime minister. He helped Greece regain Macedonia, most of the Aegean islands including Crete itself and Epirus in the northwest. And Venizelos negotiated the 1922 population-exchange agreement with Turkey under which almost a million repatriated Greeks flooded into a woefully unprepared Athens. The desperate, makeshift effort to house them expanded the city's boundaries farther than ever before, accounting for the oldest of the suburban eyesores around the capital today.

From 1936 to 1940, Greece was under the military dictatorship of Ioannis Metaxas, remembered today mainly for his resounding *óchi* (no) reply to Mussolini's surrender ultimatum in 1940. The Greeks commemorate the day, October 28, as a national holiday. Nazi Germany invaded Greece in April 1941 and by June controlled the entire country. Italian forces were placed in Athens. The people suffered greatly, but the city's monuments escaped serious damage. Unfortunately, the Greek resistance movement during the war was so politically divided that the guerrillas expended almost as much energy combatting each other as the Germans—a tragic situation familiar to students of the ancient city-states.

In October 1944, Allied forces moved into Athens and much of Greece with little opposition from the retreating Germans.

The war left Greece utterly devastated. Yet factions squabbled ceaselessly for political advantage. Communist and royalist partisans moved inexorably toward military showdown as the United States sent the first instalment of economic aid under the Truman Doctrine. Two years of savage civil war ended in late 1949 with Communist defeat. But political instability continued in Athens until 1967, when a military dictatorship seized power. Seven years later this regime of colonels crumbled. With young King Constantine in exile, a popular referendum abolished the century-old monarchy, and democracy was restored in free elections.

Only in recent years has Greece's economy picked up significantly. With foreign visitors arriving by the million and bright prospects for capital investment, Athens looks forward to its first real prosperity since ancient times. **23**

# What to See

Many of the marble treasures in this always surprising city will be almost familiar to you, but others may come as delightful "discoveries". Most famous, of course, are the ancient Greek temples and sculptures, as well as the monuments and relics of the later Roman era. Also scattered around Athens are samplings of Byzantium—not very many considering the long centuries they represent, but intriguing and beautiful. Everywhere you're likely to be caught up in the vibrant, nonstop spectacle that is Athens today. First, inevitably, to the classics.

## The Acropolis
*(Akrópolis)*

It is, you see at once, incomparable. Towering there protectively above its city, the Acropolis inspires awe now just as it did in the most distant ages.

This ten-acre rock rising 300 feet above the plain of Attica was the making of ancient Athens. Battered and incomplete though it may now be, the Acropolis possesses such majesty that it still ranks among the world's true wonders. The name means "high town", from the Greek *acro* (highest point) and *polis* (town or city). Alternately it means "citadel", which it was originally—a place of defence shared by gods, kings and heroes.

In the late Stone Age, long before history replaced legend, the Acropolis was inhabited. Strategically sited near a good, safe anchorage, it met four key requirements: it was accessible, defensible, commanded surrounding territory and had natural springs (more than 20 are known today). But after the Persian Wars, the mushrooming city in its shadow thrust its fortifications outward, and the political-social centre shifted towards the Agorá (marketplace). Gradually more emphasis was put on the sacred function of the Acropolis as cult centre of ancient Athens. In the classical era, marble replaced wood and limestone for construction on the Acropolis. Although men have wreaked far more havoc than the weather on the prize product of old Attica's quarries, the ruins of four splendid buildings, all built during the 5th century B.C., remain to excite the visitor's wonder.

The most dramatic—and romantic—time to visit this storied summit is at night during a full moon: at such periods in the summer, the gates stay open very late. Otherwise, the Acropolis and the panoramas are particularly satisfying in the late afternoon light (when photography is best). Many prefer the cool hours of early morning. On summer days, few spots in southern Europe seem as blazingly hot as the Acropolis.

The path you take up from the present-day car park generally follows the ramped course of ancient processionals. These climaxed the Panathenaic Festival, held every four years on the night of the mid-summer full moon to celebrate Athena's birthday. Garlanded priests and priestesses, flute players, cavalry troops and young maidens escorted a great ship on wheels carrying a sacred embroidered saffron robe to be offered to the city's protectress. Farm lads coaxed she-goats, ewes

1 Post Office    2 National Library    3 Byzantine Museum    4 Parliament
5 National Gardens    6 Temple of Olympian Zeus    7 Tower of the Winds

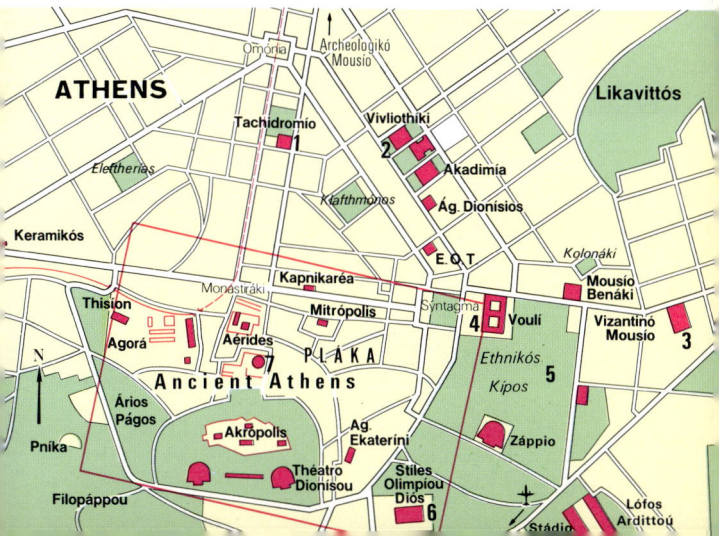

*Floodlit or sunlit, the Acropolis is always incomparably beautiful.*

and heifers up the slope—female victims for sacrifice to the virgin goddess.

The visitors' entrance is the Beulé Gate (a 3rd-century-A.D. Roman addition named after the French archaeologist who discovered it in 1852). Going past two Venetian lions, you mount a zig-zag path. The imposing marble pedestal on the left once supported a bronze four-horse Roman chariot (the *Agrippa*). From behind this 30-foot-high plinth you'll have a superb view of the Agorá and the eye-catching temple, the Thisíon.

## The Propylaea
### *(Propílea)*

Six Doric columns mark this monumental entranceway to the Acropolis. The Propylaea was planned by Pericles and his architect Mnesicles as

the most spectacular secular building in Greece, more complex than the Parthenon which it was designed to complement. Construction began in 437 B.C. but was halted five years later by the Peloponnesian War and never finished.

As you reach the porch, you'll see Ionic as well as Doric colums; this was the first building to incorporate both styles. Compare the solid majesty of the Doric with the light elegance of the Ionic. The capital of one Ionic column and a fragment of the stunning panelled ceiling—all in Pentelic marble—have been restored.

The central and largest of the gateways was for chariots and approached by a ramp; steps lead up to the four other entries destined for lesser mortals. The well-preserved building on the north (left) side housed a gallery of paintings by famous artists offered to Athena.

## The Temple of Athena Nike
(*Athiná Níki*)

High on a terrace off to the right (south-west) of the Propylaea perches this enchanting temple, the work of architect Callicrates. It enjoys a glorious panorama of the sea and distant mountains. Tiny compared with the Parthenon towards which it points, the temple of Athena Nike (also called Wingless Victory) now standing is a piece-by-piece modern reconstruction of what remained after the Turks tore down the original in 1687. Its four Ionic columns at each end are in keeping with its slight dimensions.

One of Greece's best-known legends relates that Theseus's father, King Aegeus, leapt to his death from this spot after catching sight of his son's ship. Theseus, returning triumphantly from Crete, had forgotten to change the black sails (death) for white ones, fatally misleading the old king.

Passing through the Propylaea, you emerge onto the great sloping plateau of the Acropolis. Try to imagine what it was like 2,400 years ago, when these masterworks of architecture and sculpture were going up. Scores of stone cutters, carpenters, founders and braziers, goldsmiths, ivory workers, painters, dyers, even embroiderers swarmed over this ground. For the most part they were freemen, not slaves, practitioners of nearly every art and craft known at the time.

Dominating the immediate foreground was a gigantic bronze statue of Athena under another guise—Athena Promachos, the Defender. This statue of the goddess holding shield and spear was created by Phidias to honour the victory at Marathon. It's said sailors could spot the tip of her helmet as their ships came round the gulf from Soúnion. The great statue stood here for 1,000 years, until it was carted off to Constantinople in the 6th century A.D. You'll see no more than scattered fragments of its base near an upright slab-relief of a maiden.

## The Parthenon
(*Parthenón*)

On seeing it, one automatically searches for superlatives. Perhaps the best description of the Parthenon comes from the French poet Lamartine, who

*1 Beulé Gate 2 Propylaea 3 Temple of Athena Nike 4 Parthenon 5 Erechtheion.*

called it the "most perfect poem in stone" on earth. This miracle of marbled harmony was inspired by Phidias, the sculptural, architectural and artistic genius of classical Athens. It was executed by master architects Ictinus and Callicrates and commissioned by Pericles to replace the Acropolis sanctuaries destroyed by the Persians.

Work on the Parthenon (which means Temple of the Virgin) began in 447 B.C. Marble from Mount Pentelikón (10 miles north-east of Athens), famous for its milky-white, coarse grain, was quarried specially for the temple. With the passage of centuries, it has acquired its present honey colour. Only the roof and doors were of wood. The Parthenon is 228 feet long and 101 feet wide. Its 46 exterior columns rise 34 feet, each consisting of about a dozen fluted marble drums placed one above the other.

The columns swell gently at the middle and lean slightly inward, the floor surface is convex: astonishingly, nowhere in the temple is there a straight line. All the subtly curving departures from true vertical and horizontal give life and rhythmic movement to the stone and—the architectural

stroke of genius—magnificent symmetry. By sighting along the surface from any corner, you can observe the intentional flowing arc of the temple floor. This was calculated with mathematical precision.

That overall slight inward-leaning aspect you'll notice is no optical illusion: the Parthe-

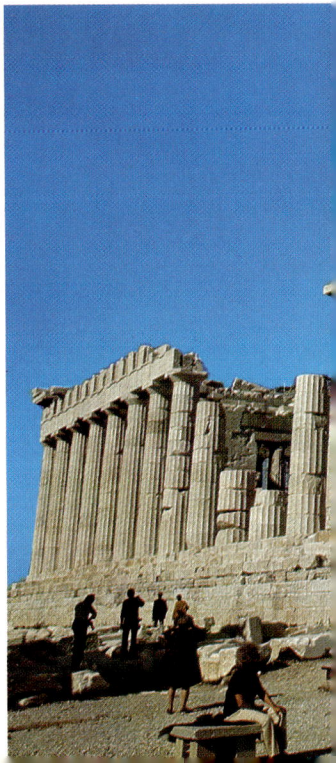

non is an unfinished pyramid with an apex projected to achieve itself at an altitude of about 3,000 feet.

Aside from its cult functions, this supreme example of the Doric temple served to symbolize Athenian imperial glory, hold the national treasury and house a precious statue. Ancient pagan temples were meant to be appreciated from the outside. The Parthenon's altar, where live offerings were slaughtered, stood

*The Parthenon: one of mankind's most outstanding achievements.*

outside the building, opposite the eastern façade. Only a few privileged persons—priests or high officials—could enter the *cella* (inner temple).

Those admitted were able to see Phidias's masterpiece, the 39-foot-high statue of Athena Parthenos, Athena the Virgin. Made of wood, it was covered with ivory and gold—which could be removed and melted down in time of dire national need. Thucydides, perhaps conservatively, says it weighed 40 talents (2,320 pounds). We'll never know—by the 4th century A.D. it had vanished forever.

Originally the Parthenon was decorated with sculptures at three levels. Very little of this remains. The renowned "Elgin Marbles", removed by the British ambassador to Constantinople at the beginning of the 19th century with Turkish permission, can be seen in the British Museum.

Above the plain beam resting on the columns were 92 square panels, called metopes, with scenes of ancient conflict. Over the centuries most have been destroyed or removed (15 are in London). The best one here shows a young Lapith (mountain tribesman from Thessaly) struggling with a centaur.

Only a fraction of the Ionic frieze that ran around the *cella,* beneath the ceiling of the colonnade, is left. It originally contained 360 sculpted human figures and 220 animals, each 3 feet high, taking part in the procession of the Panathenaic Festival. Fragments of the frieze are on view in the Acropolis Museum, the British Museum and the Louvre.

The two huge triangular pediments, now almost empty, crown the front and rear ends of the Parthenon. Once they were adorned with some 50 larger-than-life statues representing the birth of Athena, emerging fully grown from Zeus's head, and her contest with Poseidon for possession of Attica.

## The Acropolis Museum
*( Mousíon Akropóleos)*
Here you will be able to enjoy outstanding pieces of archaic and classical Greek sculpture at your ease—and get out of the sun. Every exhibit in the cool interior of this outstanding museum was found on the Acropolis.

Ancient Greek sculptors are admired as the first to portray the human form in a natural, though idealized way. They also produced some splendid animals. See, for example, the group of **four horses** (570 B.C.) in Room II, especially the two in the centre with their heads turned shyly towards one another.

A great work in the same room is the statue of a **man carrying a calf.** Note the symmetry of the calf's legs and the man's arms, the position of the calf's tail and the man's hair.

In Room IV, don't miss the **man on horseback** (560 B.C.), even though the head is a copy (the Louvre has the original). By now you'll recognize the enigmatic smile and almond-shaped eyes of the archaic period. Among several examples in this room of *kore* (young women) statues, **No. 679,** wearing a heavy shawl, or *peplos,* over her tunic, is superb.

Perhaps the museum's most enchanting work is **No. 674,** a girl with gently sloping narrow shoulders in a simple tunic, her long neck and triangular forehead framed by exquisitely modelled locks. It dates from about 500 B.C. You'll often see this reserved, slightly puzzled, slightly proud expression on the faces of

*Serene, 6th-century B.C. statue; the calf is an offering to Athena.*

young girls around the Mediterranean.

The head of the "blond youth" **(No. 689)** and the statue of the Kritios boy **(No. 698)** are examples of the transitional stage from the archaic to the classical age of sculpture. Both (from around 480 B.C.) show stirrings of individual personality expressed in art.

Room VI displays parts of the **Parthenon frieze,** with a rearing bull and meek sheep on the way to sacrifice. Watch for the splendid gods—Poseidon, Apollo and Artemis —awaiting the arrival of the Panathenaic procession.

The relief of a winged goddess removing a sandal **(No. 973),** from the temple of Athena Nike, demonstrates the incredible skill with which Greek sculptors captured the relation between dress and the human body.

Admission to the museum is free on Sundays and certain holidays (for opening times see p. 119).

## ♣ The Erechtheion
*(Erechthion)*

Across the Acropolis plateau at the northern wall stands the Erechtheion, a temple unlike 34 any other in the ancient world.

The identity of the chief architect remains something of a mystery. His task certainly was not easy. First he had to house three cults—those of Athena, Poseidon and Erechtheus—in one building; he had to work on irregular ground, meaning sharply different foundations; and finally, though much smaller than the Parthenon, his temple had to be able to hold its own. One additional difficulty: the Erechtheion, the last temple to go up on the Acropolis, was built entirely in wartime. Construction took 15 years, with dedication in 406 B.C.

This was the site of the legendary contest between Athena and Poseidon—where the goddess brought forth her olive tree (a presumed descendant grows just outside the temple's west wall) and the sea god produced a salt-water spring (see p. 11). In a corner of the north porch you'll find an uncovered hole containing a rock with markings. Some say these were made by Poseidon's trident. Another version relates that Zeus sent a lightning bolt down upon the scarred rock. There may have been an altar to the supreme god close by. And as for Erechtheus, another of the prehistoric part-man and part-snake kings of Athens, he somehow became so closely linked with Poseidon that they were worshipped together here as a kind of two-person deity.

Mythology aside, the north porch is considered a work of great architectural genius. Note its dark-blue marble frieze, panelled ceiling and the bases and capitals of its distinguished columns.

Within the temple stood an ancient olivewood statue of

*Emergency measures needed to save Erechtheion's imperilled maidens.*

**Masterpiece Mathemathics**

Sheer inspiration certainly, but ancient Greek architects also depended on mathematical exactitude to achieve their memorable works of art.

There were some definite rules: the height of a Doric column had to be 5½ times the diameter of its base; that of an Ionic column 10½ times. Another key proportion in the Doric temples—4:9. This is the ratio between the breadth and length of the Parthenon, between the shorter side of the inner precinct and its ceiling height, and between the diameter of the 46 outer columns and the distance between any two of them.

The same ratio was observed in building the Propylaea which, if completed, would have been as wide as the Parthenon is long.

Athena, said to have fallen from heaven. The saffron robe carried in the quadrennial Panathenaic procession was draped on the idol at the end of the festival. A golden lamp burned perpetually before the statue.

The Erechtheion's much-imitated door, framed by rosettes, is inside between the two centre columns. One of the elegant side columns (each 22 feet high) was taken to London by Lord Elgin. With it you'll see he removed part of the marble beam above. The capitals, with their palm-leaf patterns are particularly elaborate.

Those six bigger-than-life-sized maidens holding up the roof of the south porch are the famous **Caryatids.** Recently, after air pollution was found to have caused alarming decay, rotting the marble to a depth of ¼ inch, authorities decided to transfer five of the six statues to a museum for repair and later display. The sixth is already a copy. They

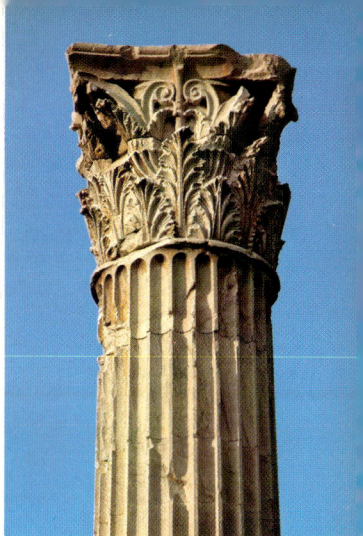

*Doric, Ionic, Corinthian columns show evolution of classical style.*

are to be replaced with fiberglass replicas.

Though named after a village near Sparta whose girls were noted in antiquity for their upright posture, the Caryatids were really Athenians. The long Ionian tunics are draped in imitation of column flutings, the baskets on the girls' heads replace capitals. The portico protected a holy place, the tomb of Athens' mythical founder-king, Cecrops.

An international appeal is underway for funds to save the Acropolis from air pollution, with proposals to remove all remaining statuary and install boardwalks for tourists away from the temples. One scheme has even suggested covering the entire Acropolis with a huge air-conditioned bubble of plastic.

Before leaving the Acropolis, succumb to the temptation to linger over the view: Athena Nike's temple faces west towards the Bay of Salamís above which Xerxes watched his fleet sink. Far beyond that are the mountains of the Peloponnesus, nestling the citadel of ancient Corinth. To the left, islands of the Saronic Gulf. Behind the violet shoulder of Hymettos *(Imittós)* to the east is Cape Soúnion. Today, traffic streams along the wide coastal road towards it; once seamen passing Soúnion strained to catch sight of the glinting gold on this venerable rock.

You can reach the Acropolis from Sýntagma Square *(Platía Syntágmatos)* by taxi, a No. 16 bus or on foot in about 25 minutes. Admission is free on Sundays and certain holidays; on other days, keep your ticket for the Acropolis Museum.

Opening times are indicated on p. 119.

# Ancient Athens

## Three Historic Hills

**Areopagus** *(Ários Págos)*
An unlikely place for murder trials, you may think as you ascend the solid rock steps of the low hill near the Acropolis. Here on the Areopagus, the war god Ares was acquitted by a divine council of killing his daughter's lover (one of Poseidon's sons)—so the legend affirms.

This is also where, according to Aeschylus's tragedy, the Areopagus or supreme court of ancient Athens judged Orestes not guilty of murdering his mother. Originally the court was composed of aristocratic archons elected for life. As democracy developed, their power was curtailed but the court's reputation for integrity remained, and it continued to have jurisdiction over murder and religious offences.

Centuries later, in A.D. 54, St. Paul preached on the Areopagus and made his first Athenian convert to Christianity.

**The Pnyx** *(Pníka)*
If not during the day, you'll certainly want to come to this terraced hillside at night for the memorable Acropolis Sound and Light performances (see p. 86). The Pnyx, meaning "tightly packed space", is where the free citizens of 5th-century-B.C. Athens met in democratic assembly. On the rocky platform here Themistocles, Pericles and Demosthenes and the other great orators of the day held forth.

**The Muses** *(Mousíon)*
Once sacred, always strategic, this hill is an obligatory stop for camera enthusiasts: there's

Stiles Olimpíou Diós

Píli Adrianoú

Singroú

Leofóros Amalías

Leof Olgas

Filellínon

Xenofóntos

Sýntagma

Nikis

Metamórfosis tou Sotíros

Petá

Nikodímou

Apóllonos

Farmáki

Ag. Ekaterini

Thalou

Lisikrátous

Frínichou

Výronos

Mnímío Lisikrátous

Mousío Laïkís Ellinikís Téchnis

Mitrópolis

Ág. Elefthérios

Filothéis

Flessa

Ermou

Kydathinéon

Ag. Ioánnis Theológos

Epicharmou

Tripódon

Ragaví

Lisiou

Dionisiou Areopagítou

Théatro Dionísou

Ág. Geórgios tou Vráchou

Mousío Akropóleos

A k r ó p o l i s

Anafiótika

Flechtou

Schallou

Epimenidou

Prytaniou

Miniskleous

Klepsidras

Kirristou

Stratonos

Théspidos

Odós

Dioskouron

Stoá Evménous

Odíon Iródou Attikoú

Kapnikaréa

Platonos

Pandrosou

Adrianou

Fólou

Pelopida

Aréos

Pandrósou

Aérides

Romaïki Agorá

Monastiráki

M

Mousío Laïkís Ellinikís Téchnis

Ermou

Iféstou

Stoá Attálou

Vrisakiou

A g o r á

Adrianou

Ários Págos

Keramikós

Thisío

Astiggos

Pýkni

Filopáppou

Pnika

N

a superb view both of the Acropolis and Athens, sloping down to the Bay of Phaleron (*Fáliro*) and Piraeus harbour. In ancient times it was dedicated to and named after the muses. But it's also known as the Hill of Philopappos, (*Lófos Filopáppou*), a Syrian prince who served as Roman counsul in Athens and died here as a citizen. The marble monument on the crest was put up about A.D. 115 in his memory.

## The Theatre of Dionysus

Here beneath the Acropolis, in this rebuilt but crumbling theatre (*Théatro Dionísou*), the plays of Sophocles, Euripides, Aeschylus and Aristophanes were first staged.

The original 5th-century-B.C. theatre had seats hacked out of the earth and a circular stone dancing stage, flush with the ground. The semi-circular orchestra of marble you see today was sculpted out by the Romans; the carved relief of scenes from Dionysus's life is the façade of a raised stage. The backdrop of stone, *skené*, gave us the word *scene*.

In classical days, wooden seats angled down to a round, white limestone orchestra with painted backstage sets slung

behind. Plato says 30,000 spectators could watch, but 17,000 seems more likely. The best seats went to top officials and religious dignitaries, whose names were carved into those front-row "thrones" of Pentelic marble (originally there were 67). The place of honour is the lion-footed throne of the high priest of Dionysus Eleftherios (named after the Attic town where the 6th-century bacchic cult began). Just behind it is the throne of Hadrian.

Greek drama originated in dance, cult and myth—particularly with the adventures of Dionysus, the god of wine, revelry and inspiration. The first recorded play was staged in 534 B.C., with actors taking specific parts and having lines to learn. The word *thespian* is derived from its author, Thespis. Incidentally, *theatre* comes from an ancient Greek word meaning "to see".

Before and after theatre, Athenians of the 2nd century B.C. and later would promenade and gossip in the **Stoa of Eumenes** (*Stoá Evménous*), a remarkable arched and two-tiered colonnade; only a section of it remains; King Eumenes II of Pergamon, the builder, lined each floor with 65 Doric columns. It ran more than 500 feet from Dionysus's theatre to the smaller and now restored **Odeon of Herodes Atticus** *(Odíon Iródou Attikoú)*. Its benefactor had donated the theatre to Athens in A.D. 161 in memory of his deceased wife. Today the city presents plays and concerts here during its Summer Festival.

*The Odeon of Herodes Atticus was Athens' first all-weather theatre.*

## The Temple of Olympian Zeus
*(Stíles Olimpíou Diós)*

As was only fitting for the ruler of the gods, this temple was the largest in ancient Greece. But it took a Roman to complete it—almost 700 years after construction started.

Back in the 6th century B.C., they say, the tyrant Pisistratus and his sons conceived of the monumental building project to keep the population too busy to plot against their

rule. But the temple was far from complete when the family regime ended. Work on it languished until Antiochus IV Epiphanes became interested in the 2nd century B.C. But the enormous monument was only finally finished off by Roman Emperor Hadrian in A.D. 132. It had 104 Corinthian columns, each 56 feet high and more than 7 feet thick. Today only 15 remain upright.

There's no trace of two gold and ivory statues Hadrian is said to have installed in the

*Surviving pillars indicate the Olympian size of Zeus' temple.*

temple: one of Zeus and the second, only *slightly* smaller, of himself.

To mark the separation of his own Athens (which he fondly called "Hadrianopolis") from the ancient city of Theseus, an arched gateway was erected facing the temple. Relatively modest in size, **Hadrian's Arch** *(Píli Adrianoú)* is thought to have been a donation from the people of Athens.

A tip: whenever you see an arch, you can be sure that the structure is not classical Greek. The Romans invented the arch a few centuries later.

## 🚶 The Agorá

The Agorá is almost as old as Athens itself. Originally the word meant "a gathering together", later the place where people met and conducted business. Sprawling under the northern walls of the Acropolis, it was the heart of the ancient "lower city", the market-place and civic centre.

Today only rubble and foundations remain of the marble or stone altars, temples, law courts, state offices, public archives, shops, concert hall, dance floor and gymnasium that stood here. A panoramic, pictorial reconstruc-tion on a pedestal by the entrance helps you visualize the Agorá in its golden days.

Barbarian invaders destroyed the buildings in the 3rd century A.D. But the Agorá's spiritual legacy lives on: politics (as understood in the West) and philosophy (based on free and rational discussion) came into being on this spot.

Socrates lived, was tried and died here. He spent most of his days at the shop of a shoemaker (who was the first to write **43**

down and publish some of Socrates' conversations). A jury of 500 Athenians convicted the philosopher. In his prison cell here he consumed the fatal dose of crushed hemlock mixed with spring water.

The huge gallery dominating the market-place is a replica of the **Stoa of Attalos** *(Stoá Attálou),* built by the King of Pergamon about the middle of the 2nd century B.C. in homage to Athenian culture. It was rebuilt from Attic marble and limestone about 20 years ago by the American School of Classical Studies in Athens, the organization that has carried on the Agorá excavations since 1931. Near this 382-foot-long painted portico, or *stoá,* the philosopher Zeno founded the school of the Stoics. And here St. Paul argued with the most sceptical audience he met in the course of his travels.

The two superimposed colonnades are made up of 90 above, while two sets of 22 columns, Ionic on the ground floor, Pergamene on the second level, divide the interiors into aisles.

*Where the philosophers once trod, sponge-sellers now ply their trade.*

The museum within (see p. 119 for opening times), has a large collection of pots, coins, household objects and fragments of pottery *(óstraka)*, on which the Athenians wrote names of prominent men they wanted to vote into exile. You'll also see a huge bronze shield captured from the Spartans during the Peloponnesian Wars and a *klirotírion*, an unusual device for assigning public duties by lot—an important feature of ancient Athenian democracy.

A path leads up a gentle hill from the Agorá to the first Greek temple entirely of marble (older ones were mostly of timber). Known popularly but inaccurately as the **Thisíon,** this very well-preserved Doric temple predates the Parthenon by a few years. Its name comes from the carved metopes atop the columns showing exploits of Theseus. Other panels depict the labours of Hercules.

The temple is properly named the Hephaestum *(Naós Iféstou)* since it was dedicated to the god of smiths. Archaeologists have confirmed there were foundries and metal-workers' shops in this area in ancient time (there are still). The formal gardens planted with myrtle and pomegranate follow, as closely as possible, the layout recommended by Roman landscapers about the time of Christ.

Returning to the Agorá entrance from the temple, you pass on your left the site of the Altar of the 12 Gods. In ancient Greece, distances from Athens were measured from this altar.

A short walk away is Keramikós, the graveyard of ancient Athens, filled with the ruins of sculptured tombstones.

# ⫟ Pláka

Drowsy and quiet by day, boisterous by night, this is the oldest quarter of Athens—and much the most charming. You'll enjoy getting lost in Pláka (most visitors do).

People have lived continuously for more than 3,000 years in this picturesque maze huddled against the northern slope of the Acropolis. Some of the narrow, winding streets follow prehistoric footpaths. To reach certain sections, you'll have to negotiate steep, stepped streets.

Sunday morning, when you'll hear priests intoning the liturgy as you wander, is perhaps the best time to visit the daytime Pláka. But any night at all you can experience Pláka's celebrated revelry— song, dance and *bouzoúki* music, charcoal-roasted *souvláki,* free-flowing *retsína.* Labels don't fit this anvil-shaped district where ancient ruins, Byzantine churches, shops, cafés, hotels, bars, nightclubs and *tavérnes* are packed into less than one quarter of a square mile.

If you lose your thread in Pláka's labyrinthine back streets, there will always be rewards—and someone to give you directions. Unexpectedly you'll come upon vivid views of the Acropolis, the Agorá, the distant peak of Mount Likavittós, Hadrian's Arch. You'll admire 19th-century houses with ochre-washed walls, green shutters and bal-

*In popular Pláka, grab the first chair: they're hard to find here!*

conies. A quiet courtyard may be filled with geraniums or hibiscus. Contrasts are everywhere.

Strictly speaking, the whole area south of Odós Ermoú is Pláka. But the heart is close to the Acropolis. To explore it, starting at Sýntagma, head down Odós Filellínon. Turn-

ing right into Kidathinéon, you'll see the 13th-century church of Metamórfosis tou Sotíros. The **Museum of Greek Folk Art** *(Mousíon Laïkís Ellinikís Téchnis)*, at No. 17, has jewellery and embroidery from the islands, and don't miss the little room with walls covered by the lively

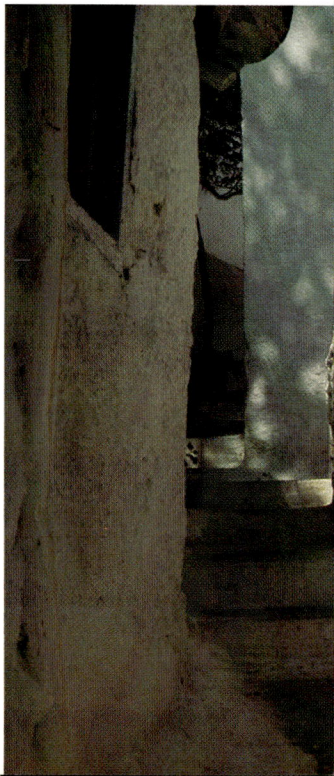

work of Theofilos Chadji-michalis, a self-taught painter with a good imagination. He painted places he never visited—from postcards. The collection also includes Byzantine crosses and jewellery.

Continuing down Kidathi-néon, turn left into Farmáki. At the end, the church of **Agía Ekateríni** (St. Catherine) sits in a sunken courtyard. The

*Right in the centre of the big city, you can still discover some havens of tranquillity more reminiscent of a country village.*

first church here was built in early Christian times. The one you see dates from the end of the 12th century. Two Ionic columns jutting up in front of palm trees are thought to be the remains of a Roman bath.

On the street bearing his name is the noted 4th-century-B.C. **monument of Lysicrates** *(Mnimíon Lisikrátous)*. The six columns are Corinthian. They support a marble dome made from a single block. On top stood a bronze tripod awarded to a boys' chorus in a 334 B.C. drama competition. A frieze shows Dionysus turning Etruscan pirates into dolphins. In the 17th century, Capuchin monks incorporated the monument in their monastery, which later became a library. It's said that Byron wrote poetry, sitting between the columns in 1809–10.

The block-long Shelley Street (named after the poet) leads to Odós Tripódon with its impressive balconied houses from the early 19th century. In ancient times, winners of Dionysian contests placed their awards—tripods filled with sacred oil—on pedestals along this street. Hence the name, "Street of the Tripods".

Following Epichármou off to the left from Tripódon, you reach a remarkable white-washed village within the city: **Anafiótika.** To cope with the severe housing shortage in Athens after Greek independence, a law was passed allowing anyone who built a house—or at least managed to get the roof up—between sunset and sunrise to occupy it. First to qualify were two stone masons from the tiny Aegean island of Anáfi. Other Anafiots, also masons, followed, building and restoring houses and churches in their native style. Today Anafiots living here on the heights of Pláka outnumber the 350 residents back on their island.

At Odós Pritaníou, ask directions up steps and lanes to two churches: **Ágios Geórgios tou Vráchou** (St. George of the Rock) has a very lovely perch, and **Ágios Simeón,** at the highest point of this village, offers a spectacular view of Athens. A stately cypress stands guard here.

Back on Pritaníou in a sunken garden is a 17th-century church dedicated to saints Cosmas and Damian, 3rd-century Arab doctors who refused fees for their services. Proceeding down the steps of Odós Erechthéos, watch on the right for the early Byzantine church

*Ancient engineering triumph – the tower told the wind and the time.*

of Ágios Ioánnis Theológos.

Turning left on Odós Erotokrítou then on Lisíou, you'll cross Odós Mnisikléous, a centre of nightlife, to Odós Thrasivoúlou. Here at the end is the church of **Panagía Chrisokastriótissa** (The Virgin Mary of the Golden Castle), which has an icon revered for miracles. One tradition says that the Greek women and children who leaped from the Acropolis in 1458 (to escape capture by the Turks) were saved by the icon from death on the rocks below.

From Odós Klepsídras you can go straight down to the **Roman Agorá.** Over to your right is the famous **Tower of the Winds** *(Aérides)*, built by Syrian architect Andronikos in the 1st century B.C. It once housed in an elaborate water **51** clock that was fed by a spring on the Acropolis. Each side of the octagonal marble tower represents one of the eight points of the compass and the corresponding wind. You'll spot Notos, the south wind, pouring water from an urn, while Zephyros, the west wind, is scattering flowers. It's said a triton—a half man, half fish—once sat atop the tower's weather vane directing the curious to the face of the prevailing wind.

Within the Roman Agorá you'll see the **Toúrkiko Djamí,** one of the two mosques left from the period of Turkish occupation.

Over on the Agorá's far side, the four Doric columns of the **Gate of Athená Archegétis** (built by Julius Caesar and Caesar Augustus) mark the main entrance to this once-central market area. One door support, now protected by a rusty iron grille, is inscribed with Emperor Hadrian's famous edict taxing olive oil. The marauding Herulians, a Gothic tribe, destroyed the Roman Agorá in A.D. 267. What's left of Hadrian's monumental library lies outside the Agorá.

On the way back to Sýntagma, aside from displays of jewellery and souvenirs in the shopping streets of Pandrósou and Ermoú, you'll find one of Athens' best-preserved Byzantine churches, **Kapnikaréa.** A modern master, Fotis Kondoglou, did the fine paintings inside this 11th-century church.

In Platía Mitropóleos is the tiny and elegantly proportioned church of **Ágios Eleththérios** (the "little Mitrópolis"), affectionately known as Our Lady Quick-to-Answer-Prayers. It was built 800 years ago from much earlier columns and beams. Over the main door, a 4th-century B.C. pagan frieze has been nearly obliterated—stamped with the Latin cross by later Christians. But you can still make out the wheels of the ship bringing Athena's robe to the Acropolis in the Panathenaic procession—all that's left of the only known artistic rendering of the famous ship.

The Mitrópolis, chief centre of worship for the Greek Orthodox Church, was completed in 1855 from the remnants of more than 70 other demolished churches. The interior supposedly resembles St. Mark's in Venice. This is where new Greek leaders are sworn in and where the famous Good Friday candlelight procession along Mitropóleos concludes.

# Modern Athens

From Mount Likavittós, far above the metropolitan bedlam, you can enjoy Athens' most spectacular panorama. An Austrian-built cable car runs up to the 910-foot summit from Odós Ploutárchou (Plutarch) in Kolonáki. You can also climb the hill yourself, but going back down on foot is, not surprisingly, preferred.

A 19th-century chapel dedicated to St. George perches at the very top of Likavittós. Just below is a visitors' pavilion where you can eat, drink or simply gaze at the stunning Acropolis and the full sweep of Athens' magical setting. On the terraces you'll find marble maps indicating all the important sights.

From Likavittós, cannon are fired on Greece's National Day and to celebrate excep-

*In this pre-eminently outdoor city many matters are settled at cafés.*

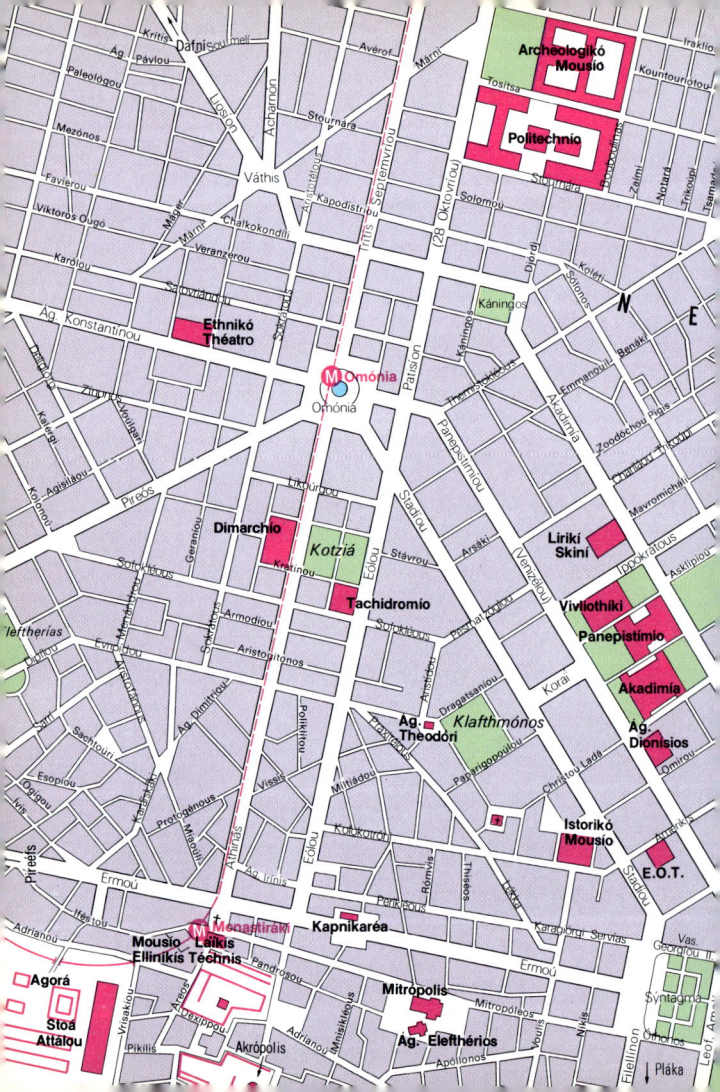

Dafni
Soumeli
Averof
Kritis
Ag. Pávlou
Marni
Iraklion
Kountouriotou
Paleológou
Tositsa
Archeologikó Mousío
Stournára
Mezónos
Váthis
Politechnío
Stisichora
Zaími
Favierou
Kapodístriou
Solomou
Notará
Trikoupi
Viktóros Ougó
Chalkokondíli
(28 Oktovríou)
Marni
Veranzérou
Dóri
Koléti
Solonos
Karólou
Derigny
Emmanouíl
Akadimías
Káningos
Zoodóchou Pigís
Ag. Konstantínou
Ethnikó Théatro
Benáki
Ematsia
Omónia
Omóniá
Lykoúrgou
Mavromicháli
Pireós
Dimarchío
Kotziá
Stadíou
Arsáki
Veranzérou
Lirikí Skiní
Sofokléous
Kratínou
Eólou
Stávrou
Vivliothíki
El. Armodíou
Panepistímio
Aristogítonos
Dragatsaníou
Akadímia
Ag. Theodóri
Klafthmónos
Korai
Ag. Dionísios
Polikléitou
Vissis
Mitádou
Papagopoúlou
Christou Ladá
Istorikó Mousío
Ermoú
Ag. Irínis
Kolokotróni
Romvis
Thiséos
Perikléous
Karaolí Servías
E.O.T.
Kapnikaréa
Ermoú
Monastiráki
Mousío Laïkís Ellinikís Téchnis
Pandrósou
Mitrópolis
Mitropóleos
Syntagma
Agorá
Adrianoú
Adrianoú
Stoá Attálou
Pikílis
Akropóleos
Ag. Eleuthérios
Apollónos
Pláka

# MODERN ATHENS

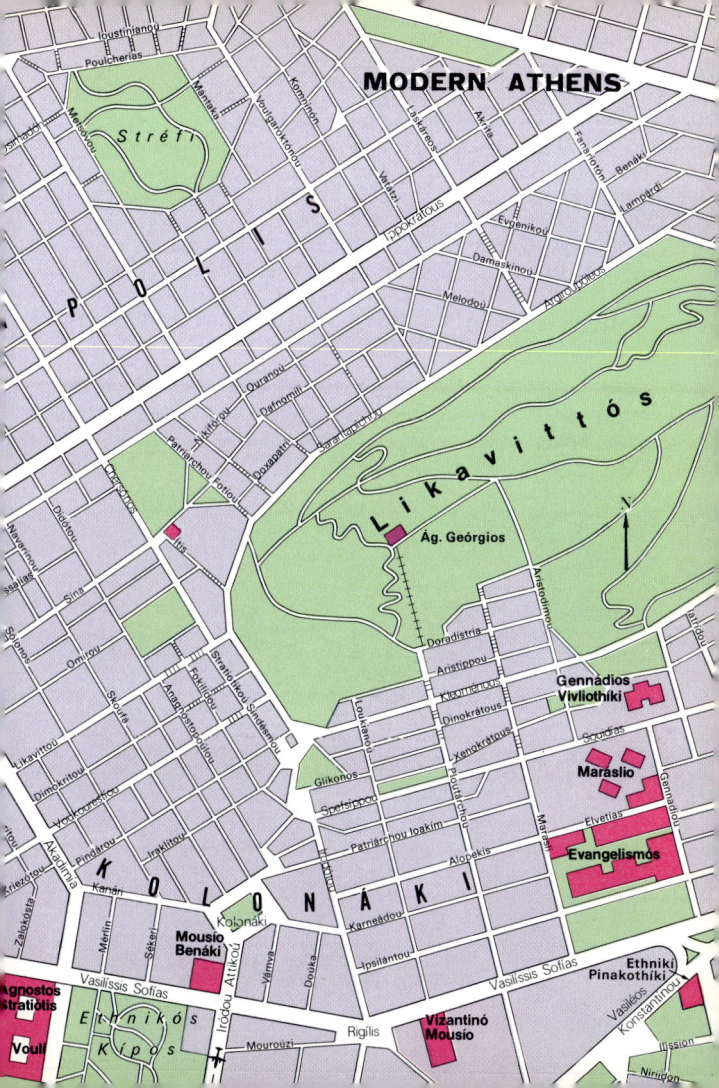

Ioustinianou
Poulcherias
*Stréfi*
Metonos
Iraklion
Kallidromiou
Ippokratous
Kominon
Voulgaroktonou
Valtetsi
Akritas
Faenorion
Benáki
Lamprou

P O L I S
Ippokratous
Evgenikou
Damaskinou
Anna Komninis

Melodoú

Ouranou
Iktínou
Dafnomili
Patriarchou Fotiou
Doxapatri

*L i k a v i t t ó s*

Ág. Geórgios

Diodorou
Neoytonou
Sina
Spevsipou
Omrou
Stratiótikou Syndesmou
Tsakalóf
Aristovoulou
Doradistria
Aristippou
Kleoménous
Dinokrátous

Gennádios
Vivliothíki

Likavitou
Dimokritou
Vryaxidou
Irakliou
Pindarou
Kanári
Merlin
Sékeri
Xenokrátous

Maráslio

Anagnostopoulou
Glikonos
Spefsipou
Patriarchou Ioakim
Alopekis

Elvetías

Evangelismós

K O L O N A K I
Karneádou
Ipsilántou
Vasilíssis Sofías

Kolonáki
Mousío
Benáki
Iródou Attikoú
Vilrna
Doúka

Anagnostopoulou
Agnostos
Stratiótis
Vouli
Vasilíssis Sofías
*Ethnikós*
*Kípos*
Mourouzi
Rigilis
Vizantinó
Mousío

Ethniki
Pinakothíki

Vasiléos Konstantínou
Ilission
Nirineon

tional occasions. You'll note the gun positions on the western slope. The hill was never included within the ancient city walls: since it had no natural springs, it was untenable for any length of time. On Orthodox Easter eve, a candlelight procession goes up to Ágios Geórgios Chapel.

You'll get your bearings in modern Athens from its two great squares: elegant Sýntagma (Constitution Square) and dowdier Omónia. They're perhaps a ten-minute stroll apart, linked directly by two major streets—Stadíou and Venizélou.

On **Sýntagma** (its name celebrates the March 1844 Greek constitution) are de luxe hotels, expensive cafés and tall glass-and-concrete buildings containing air terminals, travel agencies and international business concerns. Orange

*Greek changing of the guard: ceremonial pomp with pompoms.*

trees, palms and cypresses somehow survive the exhaust emitted by constant traffic swinging into Sýntagma from eight streets.

Across the upper, east side of the square is Greece's **Parliament** *(Vouli)*, until 1935 the royal palace. *Évzones* in traditional uniform guard a memorial to the nation's unknown soldier in the forecourt. You can watch a formal changing of this Republican Guard at 11.15 Sunday morning. Bronze shields on the marble retaining walls commemorate modern Greek military victories. There's also an engraved epitaph from Pericles' funeral oration (430 B.C.), honouring the Athenians killed in the first year of the Peloponnesian War. It's said ancient tombs lie underneath this site.

Just past the flower stalls and members' entrance to Parliament sprawls the **National Garden** *(Ethnikós Kípos)*. In this quiet oasis you'll find peacocks, exotic greenery, a children's playground and a small zoo. The busts are of modern poets. Winding paths take you to the Záppion which serves as a national exhibition hall and, in summer, an open-air stage. Breakfast at a café here is delightful.

Nestling in the hollow of Arditos Hill *(Lófos Ardittoú)*, the marble **Olympic Stadium** is on the site of the stone original built by Lycurgus in 330 B.C. (no relation to the Spartan dictator Lycurgus). At that time, Athens' fabled river, the Ilissos, flowed by this spot. In the 2nd century A.D. Emperor Hadrian introduced Rome's favourite sport here: he imported thousands of wild animals to be pitted against gladiators.

**57**

The stadium, built for the first modern Olympics in 1896, seats 70,000 people. Its length is just over 600 feet or one *stadion*. In form it's identical to the ancient U-shaped stadiums at Olympia and Delphi.

Sýntagma has always been a centre of Athenian action. Socrates' Lyceum, where Aristotle later taught, was located just to the northeast. Aristotle's nature-loving friend Theophrastos lived off the square and planted a famous Garden to the Muses. One of the original boundary stones of this shrine can be found on the northwest corner of the plaza, near the blue telephone booths. At different stages of the Second World War, the Germans and British had their headquarters on Sýntagma. An unsuccessful assassination attempt against Winston Churchill occurred here in 1944; dynamite had been planted in the sewers under the hotel where he was staying.

Along **Stadíou**, one of the city's principal shopping streets, you'll find the old parliament building which is now the National Historical Museum (on Platía Kolokotróni). Sobbing Square *(Klafthmónos)* is so named because subjects of King Otto came here to register their complaints. Just below the square is the lovely 12th-century Byzantine church of **Ágii Theódori** (Saints Theodore) with tiny stairs wrapped around a miniature pulpit.

**Omónia** (the name means "concord") is the most representative of all Athenian squares, a focal point for Greeks visiting from the countryside and many foreign tourists. Its eight streets connect the capital with main arteries to the rest of Greece: north to Thebes, Macedonia and Thrace; south to Piraeus; east to Marathón, and west to Corinth, the Peloponnesus and Patras.

Below Omónia's fountains is the central stop of the Athens underground. Take the escalator to a subterranean city with shops, restaurants, cafés, banks, a post office and information bureau. Above or below ground, Omónia is a marvellous place to absorb the variety and vitality of present-day Greece.

And nearby is where you'll probably have the most fun of all—the **markets.** Take your camera. The vegetable, fruit and herb markets somewhat

*Ice-cream? Pistachio nuts? Street snacking is an Athenian habit.*

58

illogically border Sofokléous (Sophocles), Evripídou (Euripides) and Sokrátous (Socrates) streets. But the harried housewives have no thought for the sages as they intently examine gigantic tomatoes and melons. On Armodíou you'll find livestock for sale: rabbits, chickens, peacocks, pheasants and perhaps an Athenian owl or two.

The best action is early at the fish and meat markets, along Eólou and Athinás. These covered, refrigerated halls (the fish market is constantly hosed down) have long alleys of booths and marble counters displaying everything from chops, pig's feet and sheep heads to red mullet and octopus.

Any Sunday morning at the open market in **Platía Monastiráki** you'll find some of the Mediterranean's most colourful people-watching. The quarter is alive with vendors and strollers; organ grinders push hurdy-gurdies; horse carriages bedecked with jasmine offer fresh slices of coconut for sale. The square's sunken church, the Pantánassa, was once the main place of worship at the Great Monastery founded here ten centuries ago. Facing the church on the south side of Monastiráki

is the 18th-century **Mosque of the Turkish Bazaar,** minus its minaret. After a period as a prison, it's now a branch of the Greek Folk Art Museum (*Mousíon Laïkís Ellinikís Téchnis*) housing ceramics, plates and pottery. The first-floor balcony above the former Moslem prayer hall is a fine place to watch or photograph the market bustle below.

Look for **Odós Iféstou** leading off from the metro station. This street follows the exact course of an ancient path dedicated to the god of the smiths, Hephaestus, and it is still, after more than 2,500 years, the centre for Athens artisans who work with copper, bronze and iron.

**Odós Pandrósou** runs into the square at the mosque. It is famous for its tiny shops and stalls displaying a bewildering hodge-podge of leather sandals, boots, slippers, bags, jewellery, wolfskins, worry beads and goat bells.

Worlds apart is the second broad avenue linking Omónia and Sýntagma squares—Venizélou or, more familiarly, **Panepistimíou.** Here you'll find the law courts, the National Library (*Vivliothíki*), Athens' University (*Panepistimion*), the Greek National Academy (*Akadimía*) and many fine shops. Athena and Apollo stand on the two towering Ionic columns at the Academy, whose members represent the arts and sciences.

Further along Venizélou is the former house of Heinrich Schliemann (1822–90), the son of a modest German pastor who amassed a fortune in Russia and at 36 dedicated his life to archaeology. He married a Greek, discovered the ancient palace of Troy and unearthed the tombs at Mycenae. Up under the roof you'll see engraved "Iliou Mélathron" (Palace of Troy). Today the building houses the Supreme Court.

# National Archaeological Museum

*(Archeologikón Mousíon)*

This museum holds more masterpieces of ancient art than any other in the world. Some people have spent their adult lifetimes studying the fabulous collection of sculpture, frescoes, jewels, vases, cameos, coins and everyday implements. Any visitor will want to devote at least half a day to it.

Spanning perhaps 7,000 years, the exhibits represent

*Jockey of Artemission, recovered from the sea after 20 centuries.*

every period of ancient Greek history and every site in the ancient Greek world. No matter how brief your tour, be sure to see these highlights.

The **gold death mask** of an Achaean king (popularly, Agamemnon), dating from the mid-16th century B.C., was discovered at Mycenae by Schliemann in 1876. This and other gold and ivory treasures from royal tombs are in the Mycenaean room facing the entrance hall. Look here, too, for the 15th-century-B.C. gold **Vaphio cups** depicting the capture of wild bulls, as well as an amazing—and even older—**silver libation vessel** in the shape of a bull's head. Before leaving, consider the brilliant colours of the wall frescoes from the 14th-century B.C. palace at Tirins.

For many visitors, the museum's prime attraction is its newest: the first-floor collection of astonishing **Minoan frescoes** from the volcanic island of Thera. Estimated to be 3,500 years old, they vividly illustrate the grace and sensitivity of the great sea-going civilization of Crete. The island eruption, which apparently extinguished the Minoan civilization of Crete, also buried the frescoes displayed here under many feet of volcanic ash and rock. Some believe Thera was Plato's Atlantis.

The museum's statuary rates universal acclaim. In Room 15, you'll find the famous bronze of **Poseidon**

*Golden death mask of the great Agamemnon fascinates beholders.*

(460 B.C.) about to hurl his trident. It was dredged up out of the sea in 1928 by fishermen off the island of Euboea—one of the luckiest catches in angling history. They also found the bronze **Jockey of Artemission** (2nd century B.C.), with his branded steed, on view in the Hall of the Stairs.

The earliest Greek statue cast in bronze is the open-armed **Piraeus Apollo** from about 500 B.C. Workmen digging up a street in the port city in 1959 came upon this and other early bronzes thought to be part of a forgotten shipment of booty for the Roman general Sulla in the 1st century B.C. They're in Room 45.

By the 4th century B.C., sculptors had mastered the art of individual characterization in bronze: look for the **statue of a boy** (perhaps the god Hermes) found at Marathon, the very striking **head of a philosopher** (3rd century B.C.) and the **"man from Delos"** (100 B.C.)—an incredibly lifelike head of a troubled man.

Marble statuary from the 4th century is also outstanding. The head of the goddess of health, **Hygeia,** perhaps by Praxiteles, is considered among the finest works in Greek sculpture. You may feel a more intimate appeal in the marble gravestones depicting poignant farewells to the dead: a girl removing a jewel from a case held by her maid-servant, a departing mother's last look at her child.

Hundreds of Attic vases made over an extremely long period are displayed on the second floor. Among the black-figure vases from the 6th century B.C. watch for the famous jar showing Hercules fighting the centaur Nessos. Hercules stars again in the red-figure vases from the 5th and 4th centuries B.C.—in a match with King Bousiris of Egypt who is raising an axe against the Greek hero.

The National Archaeological Museum also houses an Epigraphic Museum, a Numismatic Museum and a special collection from Santoríni.

An easy walk from Platía Omónias, the museum is between Patisíon and Tosítsa. Admission is free on Sundays and holidays. See p. 119 for opening times.

## Other Major Museums

The **Benáki Museum** (Vas. Sofías and Koumbári streets, open daily except Tuesdays) was the private mansion of a wealthy Greek art lover who left his magnificent collection **63** to the public. Don't miss the display of Greek costumes in the basement and the dazzling jewellery; items from the Bronze Age, Byzantine paintings, even a diamond pendant that belonged to Queen Christina of Sweden. You'll see mementos of Greece's war of independence, a bonnet once worn by Byron's "Maid of Athens" and lovely paintings of the Acropolis as it looked under Turkish rule.

The **Byzantine Museum** (Vas. Sofías 22, open daily except on Mondays) is the world's only museum devoted exclusively to Byzantine art. In an elegant villa built last century for a French duchess, you'll find everything you always wanted to know about Byzantine design, icons, panel paintings and sculpture. The jewellery, church ornaments and vestments are splendid: look for a 14th-century gold-thread liturgical cloth from Salonika, with the *Lamentation over the Body of Christ* on its central panel. Three rooms on the ground floor have been turned into replicas of Byzantine church interiors.

The **National Gallery of Painting** (Vas. Konstantínou 50, closed Monday) has some works attributed to El Greco and modern Greek paintings.

# Piraeus
*(Pireéfs)*

Boat buffs will love it. Even on Sundays, it's very much open for business. This, the Mediterranean's third-largest port (after Marseilles and Genoa), welcomes the longest liners and the loveliest yachts.

More than half a million people live in Piraeus, which is part of greater Athens. On its peninsula protruding into the Saronic Gulf are three natural harbours: the main port or "Great Harbour", which serves international shipping and major inter-island vessels; Pasalimáni or Zéa for the fishing fleet and big luxury yachts; and Tourkolímano

with enticing seafood restaurants ringing a tiny yacht basin.

You may not recognize the Piraeus that soared to fame with the film *Never on Sunday*—seamen's cafés and down-and-out port-front *tavérnes* are dying out, and the streets once peopled by ladies of the evening and bosun's mates now are lined with marbled banks catering for big shipping and oil clients.

But you can still find local colour. Just wander through the waterfront warren of alleyways where it seems that every possible item of food in the world is on sale, noisily. Many Aegean island residents arrive by ferry, go straight to this bazaar-like market to shop, turn around and take the next ferry home—without a nod at the rest of Piraeus or Athens over the hill.

At Zéa harbour you can watch the mending of fishing nets done with fingers and toes, for the caïques tied up at quayside. A submarine's black conning tower signals the permanent exhibit of Greek maritime history at the Nautical Museum facing the eastern end of the Zéa marina. (Piraeus began its career in the 5th century B.C., turning out 100 galleys a year for Themis-tocles' new Athenian fleet.) From Zéa a full-day tour departs each morning for the Saronic Islands (see p. 72).

And then, the jewel of Piraeus: some world-wise travellers say they visit Athens for just two reasons—the Acropolis and **Tourkolímano.** This full-moon-shaped basin, officially called Mikrolímano, has a narrow exit designed for the sleek racing yachts it berths. This is where Pericles used to go to watch boat races. Today it's where everybody goes for long, lazy lunches or dinners. You eat along the quay watching the fluffing of brightly coloured canvas and the bobbing of masts. Awnings, umbrellas, yacht pennants, signal flags blend together like daubs on an artist's palette. Included in your outdoor dining programme will be a stream of gardenia vendors, fortune tellers, guitar players strumming Theodorakis tunes, pistachio salesmen. None will press too hard. The only thieves you'll encounter on this enchanting waterfront will be the overfed cats (if you give something to one, you'll end up with 30 or 40 around you).

From the **Kastélla Hill** and its cliff-hugging road above Tourkolímano are breathtak-

N

Ag.Geórgios

*Évia*

Marathón
Néa Mákri
Ag.Andréas
Afidnés
Rafína
Vraóna

Ilía
Pentelikón
Moni
Pentélis
Kitsiá

Lávrion

**Soúnion**

Skáta
Oropoú

1413

Ag.Thomás

Ag.Triás

Inóï

Dafní

**ATHÍNE**

Fáliro
Korópi
Vá“rkiza
Saronís
Lagonísi
Anávissos

Eleísis

Skáramangás

Fáliro

Pireéfs

Glifáda
Voúla
Vouliagméni

**Delfi**

Aráchova

Livadiá

Ósios Loukás

Salámis

Ag.Marina

**Égina**

*Póros*

Póros

Idra

*Ídra*

**Thíva**

Mégara

Kinéta

Ag.Theódori

Egósthena

Plateá

Korini

Ég*ina*
Pérdika

Trizína

Loutráki

Pal.Epídavros
Methana

Ermióni

Spétses

*Spétses*

Xilókastron

Epídavros

*S  a  r  o  n  i  k  ó  s    K  ó  l  p  o  s*

*K  o  r  i  n  t  h  i  a  k  ó  s    K  ó  l  p  o  s*

**KORINTHOS**

Mikínes
Tírins

Tolón

**NÁFPLIO**

Árgos

Itéa

Ag.Pássion

2375

*P  e  l  o  p  ó  n  n  i  s  o  s*

Goúra

1812

Méga Spíleon

**TRÍPOLIS**

Megalópolis

ing views of the entire Athens area. An open-air municipal theatre of gleaming marble atop Kastélla gives performances as part of the Athens Festival.

You can reach Tourkolímano by metro to Néo Fáliro and then on foot (signs may say Mikrolímano). The trip to Piraeus is slightly longer by metro from Athens—about 25 minutes. The Piraeus metro stop is located, so the English sign says, on Platía Roúsvelt. Buses leave both Sýntagma and Omónia for Piraeus.

# Excursions

Athens is just the beginning. To fill as many half or full days as you can spare, there are marvellous experiences in all directions from the capital. By guided tour or on your own, by road or sea, here's a sampling.

## Delphi
*(Delfí)*

Perhaps the most famous classical site in Greece, Delphi basks in a setting of unparalleled beauty on the slope of Mount Parnassus. It's pos-

**68**

sible—but very tiring—to visit it in a one-day excursion from Athens; an overnight stay booked in advance is strongly recommended, either by tour bus or rental car.

For the ancient Greeks, Delphi was the "navel" of the earth—the spot where two eagles let loose by Zeus had flown from opposite ends of the world and met. Apollo, brightest and best of the gods, slew the dragon Python when he took over the precinct from the earth goddess Gaia and her daughters. The oracle he founded here, in a cleft on the rockface, was the religious and moral capital of the classical world for 200 years.

The road from Athens goes north-west, first to THEBES *(Thíva)* which shows scant trace of its spectacular past. This was the city of King Oedipus (who married his mother after killing his father), the birthplace of the lyric poet Pindar and site of the palace of legendary King Cadmus, who sowed the "dragon's teeth" which sprang from the soil as soldiers.

*From Delphi's ambiguous oracle, man sought to learn his destiny.*

Robert Harding Associates, London

LIVADIÁ (119 km. from Athens), with its "Turkish bridge", is an agreeable spot to stop. There's a clock tower presented by Lord Elgin and a mill where you can watch cotton spun on a handwheel. About 23 kilometres west of Livadiá you might detour to the monastery of **Ósios Loukás,** the most beautiful surviving example of 11th-century Byzantine architecture. The real splendours here are the mosaics—particularly the *Crucifixion* and *Descent into Hell* in the vestibule, and the *Nativity* and *Baptism* in the central dome.

After Livadiá the road climbs up into the Parnassus range. Bright-blue bee hives are scattered over the stony pastureland (Parnassus honey), and flocks of white-and-black, curly-horned goats (the region is well-known for its *féta* cheese) graze here. The low stone huts protect shepherds against the often very nasty winter weather.

If you pull off the highway near kilometre 146, you can look down into the gorge where Oedipus murdered his father, accidentally, just as the Delphic oracle had predicted. The last stop before Delphi is the beautiful terraced mountain village of **Aráchova,** famous for its colourful *flokáti* rugs, blankets and bags, wolf and fox furs and red wine.

Once at Delphi, you can park close to the museum or at the modern village of KASTRÍ, only a few minutes' walk from the ancient site. There is a moderate admission fee to both the museum and the main grounds.

Points of surpassing interest, not to be missed: the sanctuary of Apollo and the museum. Strongly recommended: a visit to the Kastalian Spring where you'll be able to taste the waters (thereby cleansing your soul), the theatre and stadium (with its sweeping, awesome view) and the sanctuary of Athena east of the main road.

In reality, Delphi's power was based on prodigious wealth: city-states and islands stretching from Syracuse in Sicily to Lydia in Asia Minor vied with each other, trying to offer the oracle the richest gifts. Wars were fought for it. And no important decisions of state from about 600 B.C. to the end of the 5th century B.C. were taken without first seeking the advice of the sacred oracle.

The Delphi **museum** contains an outstanding selection of classical and archaic pieces.

Top honours go to the world-famous bronze statue of the **Charioteer** *(Iníochos)*. This 5th-century-B.C. treasure was unearthed in 1896 after lying for more than 2,000 years under rubble from an earthquake. Astonishingly lifelike, he's heading into his victory lap: note the look of calm pride on his face and his eyes—made of onyx—still intact.

You'll also marvel at the 6th-century-B.C. **Sphinx of Naxos** and **Caryatids** from the Siphnos Treasury, and the long-haired archaic statues of **Cleovis** and **Biton.**

Among remains from the Temple of Apollo, you'll see a stone slab from the Athenian Treasury, engraved with musical notes (possibly the first) of two hymns to Apollo.

Delphi's **sanctuary** and springs lie at the foot of two scarred crags called the Fedriádes (Shining Rocks) that soar more than 4,000 feet above sea level. In ancient times, they say, blasphemers were hurled off the edge if found guilty of disrespect towards the oracle. From the ravine between these rose-coloured rocks emerges the **Kastalian Spring,** where all who came to consult the oracle had to bathe ritually.

Mounting the Sacred Way from the main entrance, you'll find ruins of a temple where the oracle held forth. In the innermost shrine, an aged peasant woman sat on a tripod—the throne of Apollo. Drugged by the intoxicating vapours that rose from a chasm, she muttered incoherent phrases, which priests "interpreted" in verses, noted for their ambiguity. A famous example: the advice to Lydian king Croesus (whose gifts included a solid gold lion weighing about 600 pounds) was that if he waged war on the Persians, he would destroy a great power. He went to war, but as it turned out it was his own power that was destroyed.

Further up the mountainside, the 2nd-century-B.C. **theatre** is still used for summer festival performances. At the highest point of the ancient site, looking down over olive groves to the brilliant blue bay of Itéa, you'll feel Delphi's magic. The **stadium** here used to hold 7,000 during the Pythian Games. In the Delphic spirit of "nothing to excess", an inscription on the south wall (in Greek) warns of penalties for drunkenness and forbids anyone to take wine out of the enclosure.

# Soúnion

Poseidon's renowned **temple** crowns this promontory 70 kilometres south of Athens, as beautiful a place to watch the sun set or rise as there is in the Aegean. Along the seaside highway you'll find excellent sandy beaches (see p. 87) and—particularly over the last 12 kilometres—spectacular seascapes.

The marble temple, with 15 of its original 34 Doric columns now standing, was built about 444 B.C. Another of stone had been started in this obviously commanding location, but the Persians destroyed it in 490 B.C. The precipice is a sheer 197-foot drop to the sea. On a clear day you can see at least seven islands.

Lord Byron, whose name you'll see carved on one of the pillars, was inspired to write the following lines:

*Place me on Sunium's marbled steep,*
*Where nothing, save the waves and I,*
*May hear our mutual murmurs sweep;*
*There, swan like, let me sing and die.*

This most popular excursion from Athens takes between 1½ and 2½ hours in each direction, depending on traffic (avoid Sundays). You can go by organized tour, local bus or rented car. Soúnion has a number of restaurants, good swimming and places to stay.

# The Saronic Islands

Take a commuter ferry or a cruise boat, but even on the shortest Athens holiday, don't miss at least one trip to a near-by island. The bustle of every embarkation and debarkation is what this traditional seafaring nation is all about. If a few goats nuzzle you on deck, you'll still enjoy the crystal-blue water.

A round-trip ticket for a Saronic Gulf *(Saronikós Kólpos)* cruise from Zéa harbour in Piraeus allows you to break your voyage wherever you like, or you can return the same day. There's no limit to how long you can stay before taking the ship back to Athens. Price, including one lunch, is reasonable.

Otherwise, most ferries leave from a quay in Piraeus's main harbour at Platía Karaïskáki near the metro station.

*Spectacular Soúnion sunsets draw poets, artists and tourists alike.*

Fares vary according to distance. If the English-language press doesn't have specific departure times for your island, ring the Piraeus Port Authority (4173-626, English spoken).

Note: Cooler weather and squalls are always possible. Take a sweater along.

## Aegina *(Égina)*

An hour and 15 minutes from Piraeus in the middle of the Saronic Gulf, Aegina is noted for pistachio nuts, pottery, local wine and a Doric temple to Aphaia. Óros, the island's mountain, serves as a barometer: if you see clouds clustering about its summit (likeliest in winter), be prepared for rain. Sponge sellers roam Aegina town's waterfront which is crammed with caïques. The AGÍA MARÍNA resort complex (15 km. from town) has a beach, water-skiing, mini-golf and a boat basin. Not far off is the restored **temple** celebrating Athen's naval victory over Persia in 480 B.C. Aegina's fleet sided with Athens in the straits of Salamís and thereby, you'll hear, helped save the world for democracy.

*White-washed houses and windmill*
**74** *cling to rocky slopes above Hydra.*

At PÉRDIKA (14 km. south of town) there's a superb beach but it may be crowded, like everything on this island where many Athenians have summer houses. If so, you can always catch the next boat to:

## Póros

Pine woods sometimes stretch all the way down to the shore on this lovely island which is separated from the mainland by a mere channel. Another popular summer resort, Póros offers splendid yachting, water-skiing, snorkelling and fishing. Within walking distance of the little port town are many secluded coves. A longer but pleasant hike will take you to the remains of a temple to Poseidon where Demosthenes, the famous Athenian orator, committed suicide in 322 B.C., rather than surrender to one of Alexander the Great's generals. Póros is 2½ hours by regular ferry from Athens, an hour and 15 minutes from Aegina.

## Hydra (Ídra)

Internationally known as an artists' colony, crammed with boutiques and discos, Hydra is the Greek answer to Capri or St. Tropez. Its spectacularly attractive **harbour** remains hidden from sea view until just before you enter the port. Then, as if a stage curtain had suddenly been drawn, HYDRA TOWN appears. Its cluster of Italianate villas rises majestically up white-washed slopes above glittering masts and dazzling sails. There are no roads and no cars, but many donkeys.

In lieu of sandy beaches, swimming is best off shaved rocks (the clarity of the water is memorable). Outside town the island is extremely bare, though you can hire a small boat to go along the north shore where you'll find occasional shade. Most visitors stick to the port animated by the international residents and "beautiful people" holidaying with them. Hydra is three to four hours by regular ferry from Athens, which gives you enough time to look at the shops, take a swim and enjoy a leisurely lunch before catching a late afternoon boat back to Athens or another one on to:

## Spétses

Last of the string of main islands, in the Argosaronic region, Spétses is wooded, hilly and shaped like a tooth. Four to five hours from Athens, it is not included on the usual one-day island tours. Transport is by donkey carriage; motor vehicles are technically not allowed. Beaches are less crowded than on Hydra and there is a lot of after-dark activity. On September 8, climaxing a week of regatta celebrations, a mock Turkish warship goes up in flames in the harbour to commemorate Spétses' proud role in the Greek war for independence.

# Daphni, Eleusis, Corinth Canal and Beyond

Some 10 kilometres (of dreary scenery) from the centre of Athens is the 11th-century Byzantine monastery at **Daphni** *(Dafní)*, celebrated for its multi-coloured mosaics. Two enormous cypresses and an olive tree mark the entrance through a tall wall.

Nothing in Western art will prepare you for the stupendous **Christ Pantocrator** in the dome—to be viewed, as the artists intended, from the entrance. On a gold background, a long-faced Jesus, with a stern but serene expression, is surrounded by 16 prophets. The other mosaics in the church are also worth lingering over; binoculars help in studying details. Look particularly for the mosaics depicting the nativity and baptism of Christ, the betrayal and the crucifixion famous for its moving portrayal of the Virgin Mary's grief.

You'll notice that saints shown on lower walls are painted. Church authorities, wise to the temptations of the flesh, used gold only above the level of raised hands.

An autumn wine festival is held on the grounds of Daphni's restored monastery.

Proceeding on the main Corinth road past depressing heavy industry and oil refineries—in an area which was Attica's most fertile during classical times—you'll approach SKARAMANGÁS with its enormous shipyards. Continue on to **Elefsís,** site of the temple of the earth goddess Demeter and the ruins of the former cult centre of the Mysteries of Eleusis.

At least 3,500 years ago, Eleusis was a sacred shrine. Not until A.D. 395, when the pagan gods were banned, did the sanctuary lose its significance. The Mysteries were celebrated every year, with a major procession along the Sacred Way between Eleusis and the Athens Acropolis.

Initiates had to swear not to reveal the secrets concern- **77** ing fertility and life after death. Aeschylus, the tragedian from Eleusis (525–456 B.C.), was almost executed when it was suspected he had given out some of the Mysteries in a play. Despite its industrial surroundings, the Eleusis museum is worth a visit.

Nero, the Roman emperor, planned to build a canal connecting the Saronic and the Corinthian gulfs. But he died before work began. In those days, the only paved road dated back to King Periander of Corinth in the 6th century B.C. Ships were winched and dragged across the isthmus—a system preferred to the perilous journey around the storm-lashed southern cape of the Peloponnesian peninsula. It wasn't until 1882 that French engineers actually started digging. It took them 11 years to construct the **Corinth Canal** (*Isthmós*, 4 miles long, 80 feet wide and 26 feet deep) which now separates mainland Greece from the Peloponessus. Only one ship can pass through at a time.

CORINTH *(Kórinthos)*, a major city in the ancient Greek world, is now a small town (pop. 20,000) of little interest to tourists. But, it's the gateway to the archaeological and scenic wonders of the Kingdom of Pelops. From Corinth (80 km. west of Athens) in one day you can visit the **Lion Gate** and the other dramatic treasures at **Mycenae**

*Like a gash from a giant cleaver, Corinth Canal links and divides.*

*(Mikínes)* high above the golden Árgos plain, the Bronze Age royal palace at **Tírins,** and the medieval fortified harbour at **Nauplia** *(Náfplio).* And close to Corinth is the sleepy village of KIRÁS VRÍSI where American archaeologists have very recently unearthed a vast and almost perfectly preserved floor mosaic dating back to the time of Julius Caesar.

Best-known wonder of the eastern Peloponnesus is the classical **theatre of Epidaurus** *(Epídavros),* built in the 4th century B.C. It remains famous for the incredible acoustics which permit even the faintest whisper to be heard in any of the 14,000 seats. Each summer, in this unforgettable setting amidst pine and olive trees, the Epidaurus Festival presents a series of ancient Greek dramas. They're in modern Greek, but you won't have to understand the words to enjoy the memorable performances.

A one-day trip including Epidaurus would be too extensive for most tourists from the Corinth area, let alone from Athens. An overnight stop in Nauplia or the seaside village of TOLÓN would allow more relaxed exploration of the Peloponnesus.

# Plain of Marathón

The site of the famous battle lies in eastern Attica about an hour from Athens by car, local bus or excursion coach. "The mountains look on Marathon and Marathon looks on the sea", Byron wrote, and so they do. The plain was known as a good place to gather fennel—*márathos* in Greek—hence the name Marathón, the plain of fennel. Ashes of the 192 Athenian dead were buried under the 30-foot *sorós,* or mound, from which you can survey the entire **battlefield.** The Persians lost 6,400 of their 25,000-man army in this catastrophic defeat for Darius. It's said that on certain nights the sound of swords clanking and the neighing of horses can still be heard. A marble platform ringed with flags marks the exact start of the 26 miles the original Marathón messenger ran to Athens, the same distance as the Olympic marathon race today.

The route to Marathón skirts Pentelikón, the mountain range where Pentelic marble for the Acropolis was quarried. There you can visit Moní Pentélis, one of Greece's richest monasteries, as well as the ancient quarries.

# What to Do

## Shopping

For luxury shopping, best values are in furs, carpets, gold and silver jewellery, embroidery, folk art and icons. Try not to buy on impulse: things are not always what they seem in Greece. The best bet is to stick to handmade items. Labour costs are still low, and the quality of rural and island handicrafts remains high.

Most shops close at 2.30 on Monday and Wednesday, often at 1.30 p.m. on Saturday. Other days they reopen after a siesta break until about 8.30 p.m.

### Rugs and Carpets

*Flokáti* rugs—priced by the kilo (a square metre weighs about 2¹/₂ kilos)—come machine-made or, preferably, hand-woven. Said to be "as natural and native to Greece as her wild mountain flowers", *flokáti* are made of pure sheep's wool shag, spun from fibres into yarn and then looped together to be processed under water. For that reason, many villages in northern Greece have sprung up at the edge of mountain streams. These rugs should be hand-dyed in solid colours with natural dyes. In Athens, go to a dealer who specializes. You'll find some in and around Sýntagma. A good tip would be to find out as much as you can about them in Athens; then, when you visit Delphi, stop and buy in Aráchova. Incidentally, Greek commercial enterprises are generally very adept at mailing abroad.

### Furs

If purchased intelligently, fur coats, stoles, capes and hats—made from pelts hand-sewn together—can be a handsome bargain. You'll find mink, muskrat, beaver, red fox, stone marten and Persian lamb. Entire villages (in Kastoriá) are given over to this industry. There's an abundance of pelts and inexpensive, subsidized labour.

The secret of the pelt-strip coat lies in the sewing, which varies in quality. Shop carefully around Sýntagma, asking questions. Be prepared to resist the hard sell in fur shops until you've established whether the sewing is completely hand-done, verified the quality and origin of the pelt, seen that it conforms to international standards.

## Jewellery

Reproductions of museum jewellery in gold and silver are definitely worth a second look. Consider copies of the Byzantine jewellery on sale in the Benáki Museum (see p. 63). There's also a shop in the National Archaeological Museum (open daily in the morning). And, for scale reproductions of sculpture, you might try across from the bus exit on Odós Iraklíou.

You'll find the best jewellery shops in the Voukourestíou and Panepistimíou area. Gold and silver are sold by weight; each item should be weighed in front of you. Workmanship and creativity involve an additional cost, tiny in relation to the real value. Some gold rings are made from two different puri-

*Look for hand-crafted items—not everything is mass produced yet.*

*Shopping in Athens can be a treat—for both palate and eye.*

## Nibbling While Shopping

Whenever you go walking in Athens, even if you intend only to window-shop, take along a bag. Aside from olives, pickles, dried meat and fish and every imaginable grain including cracked wheat, you'll pass basement grocers who specialize in nuts, beans, dried fruit (raisins, figs and peaches, for example), *ouzo*-drenched fig cake wrapped in vine leaves, spices and chocolate. Open honey (you'll need a leak-proof plastic jar) is a speciality, sold loose by the kilo.

Here's a list of some herbs, nuts and so on which might fit into your shopping bag:

Almonds – *amígdala*
Apricots – *veríkoka*
Basil – *vassilikós*
Bay – *dáfni*
Capers – *kapári*
Cinnamon – *kanélla*
Cracked wheat – *pligoúri*
Dates – *chourmás*
Figs – *síka*
Halvah (sweet nut paste) – *halvá*
Honey – *méli*
Mint – *diósmos*
Olives – *eliés*
Oregano – *rígani*
Peaches – *rodákina*
Peanuts – *fistíkia arápika*
Pistachios – *fistíkia egínis*
Raisins – *stafída sultanína*
Walnuts – *karídia*

ties; check for hollowness and correct weight-price equivalents. Enamel cannot be graded for quality, so cast a suspicious eye on anything which seems too spectacular.

## Icons and Folk Art

The *new* Museum of Greek Popular Art on Odós Kidathinéon 17 in Pláka is an obligatory stop for those interested in purchasing any Greek costumes, embroidery, buckles, leather or lace. Everything here is authentic, beautifully displayed and ticketed. Study the exhibits so that you'll be able to judge what's worth buying and avoid shoddiness and poor imitations.

The National Welfare Organization has one shop on the corner of Voukourestíou and Valaorítou (carpets are a speciality), another on Karagiórgi Servías. All merchandise has been meticulously inspected by the authorities. You'll find ceramics, embroidered silks for framing *(tsevrédes)* and other delights. Profits go to the National Welfare Fund, a worthy cause.

A word about icons: buying them is a tricky business. Make sure you find a reputable dealer who won't sell poor copies. Warped and cracked wood doesn't mean that it's old or Byzantine. These religious images can be modest, indeed humble. They should have some degree of spirituality which does not come out of a backroom secular assembly line. Note that

you must have government permission to export authentic originals and that icon smuggling is a jailable offence in Greece.

Go to Monastiráki for copper and brass, kebab skewers, mountain brigand pistols, Turkish swords, Greek bags and shawls, goat bells, wolf skins and worry beads *(kombolóïa)*. Anything made from olive wood (salad bowls in particular) should be near the top of your shopping list. To ease your way amongst the throngs, you might choose a snake-handled shepherd's crook.

For genuine folk art, some antique shops display *támata,* the silver votive offerings you'll see attached to church icons. They're mainly aluminium now, but still fashioned in the shapes of the parts of the body. Origins of this practice date to the ancient world of Zeus and Athena.

Brightly coloured plates with ship, fish and floral patterns, from Líndos on Rhodes, are good value in Athens. Sweaters are best bought on the islands where they originated—the wool is more likely to be local, not factory produced, and to contain some of the natural oil needed for warmth and wind protection.

**Bargaining**

In Monastiráki, be prepared to haggle—it's expected of you, and part of the sport. You can try it anywhere else in Athens (except at department stores and food speciality shops where certain items are price-controlled).

Approach bargaining with subtlety and a smile. Never, never seem to be in a hurry, which is fatal. Look around, leave, come back, ask the price casually, leave, come back in a day or so. Your face will be remembered. If you intend to purchase more than one item, save the last in reserve and then noticeably hesitate. Strike a deal. Certain places are delighted to accept your hard currency. Remember the "floating" exchange. Ask questions—you don't want a shopkeeper selling you glass or plastic as amber, even at a "bargain" price.

# Nightlife

Athenian after-dark entertainment centres around the *tavérnes* of Pláka, the nightclubs of Glifáda and Fáliro Bay, the cinema and the theatre. Café terraces—where most city residents spend their evenings—are not considered nightlife as such, but a sort of outdoor extension of the living room.

If you like *tavérnes, tavérna* gardens, *bouzoúki* music and Greek dancing, head for Pláka. The area around Fléssa, Lisíou and Mnisikléous streets has the densest concentration of neon tubing, mandolins, bars of all sorts, *souvlákia, retsína* and packed tables. Eating is recommended—preferably in a garden if you can find a spot. The food tastes the same almost everywhere.

Pláka included, here are some suggested locales for surveying or joining the flight of Athenian night owls.

Take a seat at a Kolonáki café terrace on the square or, in winter, the bar of a grand hotel. Habitués of smart Kolonáki are inclined to imi-

*A compelling spectacle—dancers perform with brio and dignity.*

tate jet-set creatures. Spend an evening at the race track or enjoy a seaside dinner at Tourkolímano. For those who wish to stay around the centre of town, there are about 20 dining spots nearby on the slopes of Mount Likavittós. (Menus range from international cooking through French facsimile to authentic Greek cuisine.)

The Sound and Light show starts at 9 p.m. in English on the hill of the Pnyx. From Kolonáki to the Acropolis is a ten-minute trip by taxi.

After the 45-minute presentation, you can stroll to the Dóra Strátou Theatre across the way on the Mousíon (Filopáppou Hill). The Greek dances, musical instruments and costumes are splendidly authentic, as is the internationally known company. After an hour or so of the traditional dancing, move on to Pláka, just a hop and a jump away.

Dinner-for-two at midnight under a plane tree in Pláka can be an unforgettable experience. You can order what you want from the menu and enjoy a good amount of wine without flattening your wallet too much. To round out the evening, move on to a "boîte" or a "club" for some rebétika songs or revolutionary music made popular by Mikis Theodorakis, or visit one of the popular spots in Pláka for bouzoúki music.

The really fashionable bouzoúki night clubs, featuring Greek pop stars and local folk heroes, are found along the coastal road to the airport. Try Glifáda or near the Olympic Airways terminal. These places are expensive—all have minimums, and the popular ones demand exorbitant cover charges. Most people put away huge dinners and drink well into the early morning. Exuberant Greeks, carried away with admiration for favourite lady singers, are wont to throw plates on the dance floor. This practice was banned for a period by the Greek colonels, the plates replaced by flowers as symbols of enthusiasm. Luckily for the nightclub owners, gardenias have come to be regarded as the ultimate in compliment-bestowing. They are charged for accordingly. Broken crockery and flowers automatically appear on your bill if you've used them to pay your respects.

Far less opulent, the Fáliro bouzoúki spots at Tzitzifiés (8 km. from Sýntagma along the bay toward Piraeus) are to

be recommended for their earthiness.

In the greater Athens area there are more than 300 winter (indoor) cinemas and 600 summer (outdoor) ones on roofs, in empty lots and gardens or in proper theatres. Some winter cinemas stay open, air-conditioned, during the hot months. You'll find these clustered in the middle of town, with listings and times in the local press. Most films are English, French or American with subtitles in Greek. The flourishing Greek cinema industry produces some excellent films. The outdoor cinemas don't start until after dark.

## Sports

Clean, sandy beaches are easily reached by bus, taxi or car from the centre of Athens. Obviously, the farther you go from the city, the cleaner the water, the clearer the air. For the closest good sea bathing, head along the Attica coast in the direction of Soúnion. The buses for stops as far as Várkiza (32 km.) leave from Leofóros Ólgas, opposite the main entrance to the temple of Olympian Zeus. For Soúnion and other points beyond Várkiza take the bus from Mavrommatéon, just past the Archaeological Museum.

**Astír Beach,** near Glifáda, is an organized swimming area amid pine and olive trees, operated by the National Tourist Organization (EOT). A nominal admission fee covers excellent facilities and beach attendants who'll watch your belongings. The beach is long and clean, fine for children. There are snack bars, a restaurant and very expensive bungalows for rent. One major drawback: the whistle of jets from the nearby Athens airport.

**Voúla** (20 km. from Athens) has another EOT beach, less luxurious but well run and with a lovely view over the bay. It's much quieter.

**Vouliagméni** (5 km. further south) is the show spot of the Soúnion coast. In addition to a yacht club and de luxe hotel complex, there's a public beach with water-skiing facilities. You can charter a fishing caïque at the marina. The town is named after a sulphur-springs lake which has been converted into an attractive bathing establishment (the warm, lime-coloured waters are supposed to be good for muscular aches and skin ailments).

Between the lake and Várkiza you'll find parking niches along the highway, from which you can descend to scores of rocky covelets decorating the coastline. Here swimming is off the rocks in transparent blue water. Ideal picnic spots abound, but take rubber-soled shoes. This coastal stretch is not recommended for children or poor swimmers. But the lovely beach at **Várkiza,** with pistachio trees growing almost to the shore, is perfectly safe.

At **Lagonísi, Saronís** and **Anávissos** there are more beaches still technically on the Saronic Gulf. You'll start to feel the open Aegean as you get closer to **Soúnion** with its delightful beach and excellent *tavérnes.*

Like most of Attica, the area inland before Soúnion is very dry. Be particularly careful with matches and cigarette butts. In summer, the wind can turn a spark from a piece of burning pipe tobacco into a nightmare of flame in a matter of minutes.

For less developed and less crowded beaches, try the **Marathón coast** of eastern Attica. Buses leaving Mavrommatéon take about an hour to the area of the famous battlefield. Along the coastline you'll find numerous seafood *tavérnes.* Other buses go to Ágios Andréas and Néa

Mákri on this coast, or you can take a ferry from Rafína to the island of Euboea (Évia).

Because of pollution, do not swim any closer to Athens along the northern coast of the Saronic Gulf than Kinétta or Ágii Theódori (55 to 66 km.).

Sharks have occasionally appeared in waters near Athens. Never swim alone, from a beach or a boat.

When planning a swimming excursion, keep in mind that most Greeks leave the beach early, lingering in the shade over lunch perhaps, but rarely returning to swim. As a result, bathing areas are much less crowded in the afternoon. This is even true on Sundays, reverentially reserved by Greek families for beach outings. Along all coastal roads, be prepared for heavy Sunday traffic. Boats returning to Piraeus on Sunday summer evenings are also jammed. Stay in Athens, or don't come back from your island until Monday.

Certain hotels around town

*For a lazy sail or serious race, boats abound on the Athens coast.*

have pools which non-guests may use, expensively. In Piraeus you won't want to enter the sea, but at the Zéa yacht marina you'll find an attractive Olympic pool with constantly changing salt water, excellent facilities and a restaurant. There is an admission fee; children under eight are not admitted.

## Sailing

For information contact the Sea-Horse Club at Ágios Nikólaos 75, Glifáda (tel. 894-8700). It is run by Dutchmen who rent out small craft to experienced sailors.

## Yacht Charters

Cruising the Aegean islands can be a magnificent experience. The National Tourist Organization will put you on the track of reputable brokers. Ads are placed daily in the English-language press and in *The Athenian* magazine.

## Skin Diving and Underwater Fishing

The Ágios Kosmás Sports Centre (tel. 981-5572) will have current information. Spear guns are forbidden on public beaches; fishing with air tanks is forbidden here. Along the Attica coast, snorkelling is not very good.

## Water-Skiing

Ask about facilities at Astír Beach, Glifáda or the Sports Centre at Ágios Kosmás opposite the Olympic Airways terminal on the coastal road. At times a ski school operates at Astír. But at Vouliagméni, it's a speciality. On the island of Aegina, try Agía Marína. On Póros, you should find serious skiing on the secluded bay near the town. Wherever you find it, water-skiing rates will reflect the very high price of petrol in Greece.

## Tennis

Courts are available to the public and racquets may be rented at the Ágios Kosmás Sports Centre which also has facilities for mini-golf, volleyball and basketball. You'll also find courts on the beach at Voúla and Vouliagméni.

## Golf

There's an 18-hole course at the Glifáda Golf Club just past the airport. A visitor's membership is available for a limited period. Fees on weekends are slightly higher. Golf carts, clubs and caddies are for hire. For information, telephone 894-6820. Some golfers wear earplugs to lessen the noise of jetliners landing and taking off.

## Football

International soccer and competition in the Greek football league can be watched, in season, at the enormous Karaïskáki stadium. For tickets, see your hotel desk. Be prepared to pay large sums for seats, since football is Greece's number-one sport. To get to the stadium, take the underground (Néo Fáliro stop).

## Horse Racing

The Athens Race Course *(Ippódromos)* is located at the bottom of Singroú just before the sea. Racing with betting takes place every Wednesday and Saturday, late afternoons in the winter, evenings in summer. Restaurants and snack bars are on the premises. Whether you bet or not, this is a very pleasant way to spend a few hours, particularly in the summer.

## Snow Skiing

Winter sports facilities, including a ski-lift, are found on Mount Parnassus. The villages of Delphi and Aráchova have become, in effect, ski resorts. For information, contact the Greek Alpine Club through your hotel desk in Athens, or go directly to their office in Aráchova.

# Wining and Dining

Although Athens can hardly claim to be a gourmet's paradise, you'll find eating here very satisfying, perhaps even exciting—and often in a pleasant outdoor setting. Excellent natural ingredients from all over Greece are used in restaurants. Delicious grilled fish, country salads, baked meat and exquisite fruit have good, fresh flavour.*

Give the more interesting specialities a try: garlic-yoghurt-cucumber dip *(dzadzíki)*, fried octopus, goat's-milk cheese *(féta)* steeped in olive oil and brine, garlic mashed potatoes *(skordaliá)* and the omnipresent resin-flavoured wine *(retsína)*. If you visit Athens at Christmas or Easter, or are invited to a local wedding, don't fail to taste innards soup *(magirítsa)*—in fact, you'll be considered rude if you fail to mop up your plate.

Athenians like spitted meat, olives, the head and eyes of fish. They also like fine French cuisine, hamburgers, pizza and pistachio nuts. With so many restaurants and *tavérnes*

---

* For more information on wining and dining in Greece, consult the Berlitz EUROPEAN MENU READER.

around, you won't want to be confined to a full-board plan at a hotel (where the menu's likely to be routinely "continental"). Some of the very best eating places are in residential quarters away from the usual tourist haunts—ask an Athenian.

And don't worry about a language problem: in most Greek restaurants it's common practice for the customer to enter the kitchen and inspect the array of pots and pans on the stove, or even peek inside the refrigerator. When you've decided what you'd like, just point it out. A half-portion is *olígo* (a little).

If you're bashful or lazy about venturing into the kitchen, ask for a menu (usually printed in at least one major European language as well as Greek transcribed in the Latin alphabet). Incidentally, unless your waiter has already introduced himself as Spíros or Giórgos, call him *garçon*. Athenians use the French word, properly pronounced.

Restaurants or the less elaborate *tavérnes* open as early as noon, but don't become very crowded before 2 p.m. Although dinner is served from 8 p.m., most Greeks eat much later. Restaurants in town or in the cooler surrounding countryside are in full swing long past midnight. Hotels try to maintain earlier mealtimes to accommodate northern habits.

All eating establishments (except those in the luxury class), are price-controlled according to category. The service charge is included in the bill, but you should leave a bit extra for the waiter. If a youngster brings iced water or an ashtray, or cleans off the table, it's customary to give him a few drachmas as you leave.

## Greek Specialities

Greek cooking is usually honest, at times imaginative. You may notice Turkish or Arab influences. Olive oil, lemon, tomatoes, onion, garlic, cheese and such herbs as oregano are inevitable features of the culinary landscape.

Most restaurants of all categories will serve these dishes:

*Soúpa avgolémono:* the best-known Greek soup, made with chicken or meat stock, eggs and rice and flavoured

*Pegged up to dry out, octopus is later served as a local delicacy.*

with lemon juice. Delightfully refreshing, it may be brought on just before the last course—to help settle the stomach. A similar sauce with eggs and lemon often appears with other dishes.

*Dzadzíki:* a provocative yoghurt dip featuring garlic and grated or finely sliced cucumbers. It's served cold, usually with other *mezédes* (snacks) such as *taramosaláta* and *dolmádes.*

*Taramosaláta:* a spread spreading in popularity around the world, made with *taramá* (grey mullet roe) which, with mashed potatoes, olive oil, lemon juice or perhaps moistened bread, is beaten into a smooth pink paste. Greeks eat it on bread chunks or on lettuce as a salad.

*Dolmádes:* grape leaves stuffed with minced meat (often lamb) and rice and seasoned with grated onion and herbs. A Middle-Eastern favourite, they're often served hot in Greece with an *avgolémono* sauce.

*Keftédes:* meatballs, usually of minced beef and lamb, with grated onion, cinnamon, crushed mint leaves and oregano. They're baked or deep-fried in oil.

*Moussaká:* one of the most **94** popular Greek dishes. Alter-nate layers of sliced aubergine (eggplant) and minced meat are baked with a white sauce and grated cheese.

*Kolokíthia gemistá me rízi ke kimá:* marrow (zucchini) stuffed with rice and minced meat.

*Kotópoulo psitó (sti soúvla):* roast chicken (spit-roasted).

## Seafood and Tourkolímano (Mikrolímano)

The bounty of Greece's waters can be sampled all over Athens, but you'll enjoy it most at Piraeus's little yacht harbour of Tourkolímano (see p. 66). At the string of dockside restaurants there, you'll unfailingly find seamen's *mezedákia*—octopus chunks, clams, oysters, sea urchins and whitebait. Or *psarósoupa* or *kakaviá,* a fisherman's soup that rivals better-known cousins around the Mediterranean. A local speciality is *garídes giouvétsi,* shrimps in tomato sauce with *féta,* cooked in white wine and served in an earthenware pot.

Fish in Greece is usually grilled or fried, basted with oil and served with lemon juice. You're expected to go into the kitchen, select your fish and watch as it's weighed; the charge is by the kilo. Aside from all the frisky, fresh fish, you may see others stored in drawers of the huge refrigerators. They've been frozen to prevent spoiling, the normal practice to avoid waste in this hot climate. If that day's catch of *kéfalos* (grey mullet) had to be frozen, no one will try to hide the fact. But fresh or freshly frozen, fish and seafood are suprisingly expensive—the boats must go ever further to find worthwhile catches.

Among the most common items on Athens menus:

*Astakós:* Mediterranean lobster or crayfish, often served with oil and lemon sauce or garlic mayonnaise. Clawless or not, the price is very high.

*Barboúni:* red mullet, considered by Greeks to be the best of all fish. It's also expensive. Usually dusted with flour and fried.

*Chtapódi:* octopus, usually cut in slices and fried or boiled.

*Fagrí:* sea bream, it's best baked.

*Garídes:* shrimps.

*Glóssa:* sole (smaller than the oceanic variety).

*Kalamaráki:* squid, always tasty, often surprisingly tender.

*Kéfalos:* grey mullet.

*Lithríni:* spotted bream.

*Marídes:* whitebait, similar to the Atlantic sprat.

## Other Courses

Practically every restaurant in the country serves the reliable Greek "village" salad *(saláta choriátiki)* of sliced cucumbers, tomatoes, green peppers, onions, radishes, olives, topped with *féta*. Or if you prefer, you can have a separate order of any of these ingredients. In many *tavérnes,* you dress your own salad. You'll see Greeks drowning theirs in olive oil, ignoring vinegar.

Fruit is a real delight. *Pepóni* (a melon with a taste somewhere between cantaloupe and honey dew) and *karpoúzi* (watermelon) are mouth-watering. So are the peaches, oranges, figs (best in August) and seedless grapes. You can order a bowl of mixed fruit for any number of people—it should arrive at your table peeled, cut and ready to eat.

The ubiquitous *féta* is the most distinctive of Greek cheeses. But hard yellow types—*kaséri, kefalotíri, kefalograviéra* or *kapnistó*—available in many restaurants and shops are good for snacks. Better restaurants may have imported cheeses.

## Snacks

In many parts of Athens, you'll work up an appetite just walking along the street. The odours wafting from snack bars, the vendors with their nuts and sweets are difficult to resist.

At a *psistariá* (place specializing in grilled foods), you'll find the familiar favourite *souvlákia*—pieces of veal, lamb or pork and vegetables cooked on a skewer *(soúvla)*. Even better, and more portable, is *souvláki me píta*—grilled meat, tomatoes, peppers and onions topped with *dzadzíki* and wrapped in round, flat bread *(píta)*. Slices off a large cone of lamb or other meat roasted on a rotating spit are usually called *donér kebáb*. You can also get spicy sausages and patties of minced meat in various shapes.

For less piquant treats, head for a *galaktopolío,* a dairy counter selling natural yoghurt (delicious), milk, butter and pastries, including cheese-filled *tirópita*. At these little shops you can get the makings of a do-it-yourself Greek breakfast: honey to put on your yoghurt, a plastic spoon, and perhaps crusty bread. Then repair to a nearby café table and enjoy the morning sun.

## Cafés

When in Athens, be lazy. People-watch. Join the Athenians who love to sit at cafés, drink a coffee or an aperitif, stare and gossip. Meet in the evening at Omónia, Kolonáki or Sýntagma at about 9—earlier you'd be bumping into Athenians on their way home from work. In summer go early to Tourkolímano and see the sunset, listen to the boats. Athenians interested in the latest rumours usually gather at one of the cafés at the upper end of Odós Panepistimiou.

With your drink you'll also be served a tiny plate of *mezédes* (hors d'œuvre)—usually cheese, olives, tomatoes, *taramosaláta,* salami or slices of fried octopus. The *mezé* will vary according to the quality of the café. But it will always appear when *oúzo,* the national drink, is served.

Some cafés and tea-shops *(zacharoplastío)* serve sweets. Several feature *fíllo*—flaky, paper-thin pastry. The best known is *baklavá,* which is *fíllo* filled with chopped almonds and walnuts and steeped in honey or syrup. *Kataífi* may look like shredded-wheat breakfast food, but the similarity stops there: it, too, is made of *fíllo* and honey.

Ice-cream, understandably

popular in Greece, is excellent. Cafés and tea-shops serve it in various ways. A *graníta,* scoops of home-made water ice, will be less filling.

**Drinks**

Clear, aniseed-flavoured *oúzo* —reminiscent of French pastis—has a kick to it. Drink it in moderation and nibble something at the same time, as the Athenians do. It's usually mixed with chilled water (turning a milky colour), but you can have it with ice *(me págo)* or neat *(skéto).*

Whisky, gin and vodka are expensive (tonic is available). The Greeks make very good vermouth, both sweet and dry.

When you sip your first glass of *retsína,* the classic Greek white wine, you may think the waiter has misunderstood your order. Or that, perhaps, you've wandered into a paint shop by mistake. This tangy wine is flavoured with pine resin, giving it a slight turpentine-like taste. Don't be alarmed. The Greeks have been drinking—and savouring—it since ancient times.

Greek wines were originally transported and stored in

*Walking around Athens you'll find endless between-meal temptations.*

pine-wood casks, sealed with resin. Later, when vats and bottles replaced the casks, the Greeks continued to resinate their wines to obtain this special flavour. Greeks say it rarely causes hangovers and helps to digest rich, oily foods.

The Athens region's *retsína*, particularly from the villages of Koropí and Pikérmi, is renowned as the genuine article. But there's not much of it left. Much *retsína* today is chemically aged, and instant resin flavour added without assistance from the old-fashioned pine barrels. If you happen on a *tavérna* which still serves open *retsína* from the

cask, you'll appreciate the difference.

Rosé wine, known locally as *kokkinélli*, is considered a delicacy. Ask for *Céllar*, which also produces a good non-resinated white wine.

If you find you'd rather stick with the more traditional wine flavour, there are many very adequate Greek choices. *Sánta Hélena* is a good dry white; *Pallíni* (a village in Attica) produces tender grapes which rival some French whites. *Boutári* and *Náoussa* reds and whites—grace many a Greek table. *Deméstica* red and white wines are popular at home and can be

found in wine shops abroad.

Greek beer *(bíra)* has German origins and is excellent. German and Dutch breweries bottle beer in Greece.

The best known foreign after-dinner drinks are available but expensive in Athens. Greek brandies, rather sweet, cost much less.

If you prefer something non-alcoholic, there are cola drinks and good bottled orange and lemon *(portokaláda, lemonáda)*. Greek coffee, actually Turkish in origin, is boiled to order in a long-handled copper or aluminium pot called a *bríki* and poured, grounds and all, into your little cup. Ask for *éna varí glikó* if you want it sweet; *éna métrio,* medium, or *éna skéto,* no sugar. Wait a few minutes before sipping to allow the grounds to settle. Traditionally, a glass of cold water is served with the coffee.

If you become desperate for a cup of coffee, home-style, your best bet is instant coffee, referred to everywhere as *nes.* Some better cafés also serve espresso. Iced coffee, called *frappé,* is a popular hot-weather refresher.

As for tea, don't expect it served in a pot. The water will be good and hot, but a tea bag will probably be floating in it.

---

## To Help You Order

Could we have a table?

**Tha boroúsame na échoume éna trapézi?**

I'd like a/an/some…

**Tha íthela…**

| | | | |
|---|---|---|---|
| beer | **mía bíra** | mineral water | **metallikó neró** |
| bread | **psomí** | | |
| coffee | **éna kafé** | napkin | **éna trapezo-mándilo** |
| cutlery | **machero-pírouna** | potatoes | **patátes** |
| dessert | **éna glikó** | rice | **rízi** |
| fish | **psári** | salad | **mía saláta** |
| fruit | **froúta** | soup | **mía soúpa** |
| glass | **éna potíri** | sugar | **záchari** |
| ice-cream | **éna pagotó** | tea | **éna tsái** |
| meat | **kréas** | (iced) water | **(pagoméno) neró** |
| milk | **gála** | wine | **krasí** |

99

# How to Get There

## BY AIR

### Scheduled Flights

**From the British Isles:** There are frequent daily non-stop flights to Athens from London, with connections to and from Manchester, Dublin, Edinburgh and Aberdeen.

Provided they make their reservations and pay well in advance, Athens-bound travellers can take advantage of the economical APEX (Advance Purchase Excursion) fare. Young people under 21 as well as students under 26 are eligible for special rates.

**From North America:** There are daily non-stop flights from New York and connections via Paris, Scandinavia or Rome from major airports of the U.S. and Canada.

The economy-minded traveller is confronted with an enormous choice of special fares that offer savings ranging from the substantial to the sensational. Some excursion tickets are part of a package that includes hotel and other land arrangements (see below).

**From Australia:** Special excursion fares are available for Athens with a fair choice of direct flights and connections. Alternatively, it's possible to take advantage of one of the reduced fares to London and pay a surcharge for a stopover in Athens.

### Charter Flights and Package Tours

**From the British Isles:** All-inclusive holidays to Athens are offered by many of the major tour operators. Several include a number of days in the capital and the remainder of the stay on one of the Greek islands. Despite their limitations, these arrangements generally mean good value for money, but be sure to use a reliable travel agent.

**From North America:** Package arrangements are usually on scheduled flights. Inquire about the Group Inclusive Tour (GIT), One-Stop Tour Charter (OTC) and Advance Booking Charter (ABC) plans. Your travel agent will help you explore all the options.

## BY ROAD

At fares only slightly lower than some air tickets, express coach services operate between London and Athens, with a travel time of three days as against about three hours by air.

For motorists, the preferred itinerary is from Dover to either Ostend or Zeebrugge and on to Greece via the motorways skirting Brussels, Munich, Belgrade and Niš. You can reduce driving time either by loading yourself and your car on an auto-train for part of the journey (expensive) or by driving through France and Italy and taking one of the Italy–Greece ferries for the final stage of the trip (see below).

## BY SEA

In summer, passenger and car-ferries operate frequently between certain Italian ports and Greece. The most popular routes for Athens-bound travellers are Venice–Patras and Brindisi–Patras, though you can also embark at Ancona, Bari and Otranto.

## BY RAIL

The main rail link between the United Kingdom and Greece is by the Simplon Express which takes you through Ostend, Brussels, Cologne, Munich, Salzburg, Ljubljana and Belgrade to Athens.

# When to Go

For most of the year, Athens enjoys a truly Mediterranean climate, with warm to hot days and mild nights. However, temperatures can fall to the low 40s in winter, so go prepared with warm clothing. In July and August, the main tourist season, Athens can be stiflingly hot by day—with not much respite at night. At this time of year a couple of days on one of the islands will come as a welcome relief.

| | | J | F | M | A | M | J | J | A | S | O | N | D |
|---|---|---|---|---|---|---|---|---|---|---|---|---|---|
| **Air temperature** | | | | | | | | | | | | | |
| Max. | F | 54 | 54 | 60 | 66 | 76 | 84 | 90 | 90 | 84 | 74 | 65 | 58 |
| | C | 12 | 12 | 16 | 19 | 25 | 29 | 33 | 33 | 29 | 23 | 20 | 15 |
| Min. | F | 44 | 44 | 46 | 52 | 60 | 66 | 72 | 72 | 66 | 60 | 52 | 46 |
| | C | 7 | 7 | 8 | 11 | 16 | 19 | 23 | 23 | 19 | 16 | 11 | 8 |
| **Water temperature (Piraeus)** | | | | | | | | | | | | | |
| | F | 57 | 57 | 55 | 59 | 64 | 72 | 77 | 77 | 75 | 72 | 64 | 61 |
| | C | 14 | 14 | 13 | 15 | 18 | 22 | 25 | 25 | 24 | 22 | 18 | 16 |

# Planning Your Budget

To give you an idea of what to expect, here are some average prices in Greek drachmas. However, take into account that all prices must be regarded as approximate, as inflation creeps relentlessly up.

**Baby-sitters:** 150–250 drs. per hour.

**Boat excursions** (one way): Piraeus to Hydra 180–250 drs., Piraeus to Spétses 220–300 drs.

**Car hire** (high season July–Sept.): *Fiat 127* 560 drs. per day, 7.70 drs. per km., 11,600 drs. per week with unlimited mileage; *VW Polo* 750 drs. per day, 9 drs. per km., 14,300 drs. per week with unlimited mileage; *Minibus* 1,820 drs. per day, 17.70 drs per km. (no unlimited mileage).

**Cigarettes:** Greek 20–30 drs., foreign brands 60–70 drs. for a packet of 20; tobacco 70–150 drs. for 25 grams.

**City transport:** Bus ticket (one way) 10 drs., after midnight 15 drs., underground 10–20 drs. Airport buses to centre (one way) 45 drs.

**Entertainment:** *bouzoúki* (including an *oúzo*) 150–250 drs., *discotheque* (admission and first drink) 200–350 drs., *cinema* 70–100 drs., *sound and light* 80 drs.

**Guides:** half day 1,700 drs., full day 3,500 drs.

**Hairdressers:** haircut 200–500 drs., shampoo and set 300–600 drs., permanent wave 1,000–2,000 drs; **Barbers:** haircut 200–300 drs.

**Hotels** (double room with bath, summer season): Class A 1,400–2,000 drs., Class B 1,100–1,600 drs., Class C 750–1,200 drs., Class D 450–600 drs.

**Meals and drinks:** Continental breakfast 90 drs., lunch/dinner in fairly good establishment 300–500 drs., coffee (instant) 20–30 drs., Greek brandy 40 drs., *oúzo* 30 drs., *souvlákia* (per skewer) 15 drs., beer 35–50 drs., soft drinks 20–30 drs.

**Taxis:** The minimum fare is 25 drs.; meter starts at 10 drs., extra charge from airport, ports, train stations 10 drs., luggage per piece 10 drs., night rate from midnight to 7 a.m. an additional 10 drs. not shown on the meter.

# BLUEPRINT for a Perfect Trip

## An A-Z Summary of Practical Information and Facts

## Contents

A star (*) following an entry indicates that relevant prices are to be found on page 102.

Listed after many entries is an equivalent Greek expression, usually in the singular, plus a number of phrases that may come in handy during your stay in Athens.

Although every effort has been made to ensure the accuracy of the information contained in this book, changes will inevitably occur, and we would be pleased to hear of any new developments.

**A** **AIRPORT** (ΑΕΡΟΔΡΟΜΙΟ—*aerodrómio*). Athens airport, only 10 kilometres from the capital, has two separate terminals reached by different buses: the East Terminal which serves all international airlines except Olympic Airways (the Greek national airline); and the West Terminal which handles only Olympic flights—foreign and domestic. Domestic flights are operated exclusively by Olympic Airways.

Olympic Airways runs a free shuttle service between the two airport terminals every hour from 8 a.m. to 8 p.m.

Both terminals contain offices of the National Tourist Organization (EOT), a currency exchange office, hotel-reservation counters, newsstands, car-hire agencies and refreshment facilities, but only the East Terminal has a duty-free shop. Porters are plentiful.

There's a direct bus service from the airport to the centre of town. Coaches leave the East Terminal every half hour (from 6 a.m. to midnight) for Leofóros Amalías 4, just off Sýntagma. A West Terminal service leaves for the Olympic town office at Leofóros Singroú 96–100 every half hour (from 6 a.m. to midnight).

A taxi ride to the centre of town takes about 25 minutes.

| | |
|---|---|
| Porter! | **Achthofóre!** |
| Taxi! | **Taxí!** |
| Where's the bus for …? | **Pou íne to leoforío giá …?** |

**ALPHABET.** See also LANGUAGE, and box on page 11. The exotic letters of the Greek alphabet needn't be a mystery to you. The table below lists the Greek letters in their capital and small forms, followed by the letters they correspond to in English. In cases where there are various possibilities, we give pronunciation examples.

| | | | | | | | | |
|---|---|---|---|---|---|---|---|---|
| **A** | α | a | as in b**a**r | | **Ξ** | ξ | x | like **ks** in than**ks** |
| **B** | β | v | | | **O** | o | o | as in b**o**ne |
| **Γ** | γ | g | as in **g**o* | | **Π** | π | p | |
| **Δ** | δ | d | like **th** in **th**is | | **P** | ρ | r | |
| **E** | ε | e | as in g**e**t | | **Σ** | σ, ς | s | as in ki**ss** |
| **Z** | ζ | z | | | **T** | τ | t | |
| **H** | η | i | like **ee** in m**ee**t | | **Y** | υ | i | like **ee** in m**ee**t |
| **Θ** | θ | th | as in **th**in | | **Φ** | φ | f | |
| **I** | ι | i | like **ee** in m**ee**t | | **X** | χ | ch | as in Scottish lo**ch** |
| **K** | κ | k | | | **Ψ** | ψ | ps | as in ti**ps**y |
| **Λ** | λ | l | | | **Ω** | ω | o | as in b**o**ne |
| **M** | μ | m | | | **OY** | ου | ou | as in s**ou**p |
| **N** | ν | n | | | | | | |

**ANTIQUITIES** *(archéa)*. Antiquities may be exported only with the approval of the Greek Archaeological Service (at Polignótou 13) and after paying a fee. Anyone caught smuggling out an artefact may receive a long prison sentence and a stiff fine, and the item will be confiscated. Travellers purchasing an antiquity should get the dealer to obtain an export permit. For initial inquiries and all further information on steps to follow, contact the General Department of Antiquities, Odós Aristídou 14 (tel.: 3243-010).

**BABY-SITTERS*** *("baby-sitter")*. You'll see advertisements by agencies in the local English-language publications. Check with your hotel receptionist to find a suitable one.

Can you get me a baby-sitter for tonight?

**Boríte na mou vríte mía "baby-sitter" giapópse?**

**BOAT SERVICES*.** Piraeus is the departure point for local ferryboats to Aegina. Póros, Hydra (Ídra) and Spétses. Sailings are frequent (15 daily to Aegina in summer) and their number is increased

---

* except before **i-** and **e-**sounds, when it's pronounced like **y** in **y**es

**B**

on weekends and on holidays. Hydra is $3\frac{1}{4}$ hours from Piraeus, Spétses about 4. Boats dock along Aktí Posidónos (Poseidon quay), not far from the Piraeus underground (subway) station. Some of the boats take on cars. Contact your hotel desk or travel agent for details.

In the summer months, there's also a hovercraft service from Zéa harbour to Póros, Hydra and Spétses. It's faster but considerably more expensive.

Ferry-boat services between the Attica mainland and the island of Salamís leave from Pérama, north of Piraeus.

There may be as many as four fare classes, but for daytime trips most tourists find the cheapest perfectly adequate. First or second class cabins may be preferable overnight.

If you're watching your travel budget, it's wise to buy food and drink ashore before departure: even snack and soft-drink prices on Aegean boats are high. On the other hand, passenger fares in Greek waters are very low by world standards. If you take your car, you'll have to pay the stated charge plus an extra loading fee.

**C**

**CAMPING** (ΚΑΜΠΙΝΓΚ—*"camping"*). Camping in Greece is only permitted on organized sites. There are 11 of them on the Attica mainland, some open all year round. Rates vary depending on season, facilities and location. For a full listing of camping sites and facilities, contact the EOT office in Sýntagma or the National Tourist Office of Greece in your country (see TOURIST INFORMATION OFFICES).

| | |
|---|---|
| May we camp here? | **Boroúme na kataskinósoume edó?** |
| We've a tent. | **Échoume mía skiní.** |
| Can I hire/buy | **Boró na nikiáso/agoráso** |
| a sleeping bag? | **éna "sleeping-bag"?** |

**CAR HIRE\*** (ΕΝΟΙΚΙΑΣΕΙΣ ΑΥΤΟΚΙΝΗΤΩΝ—*enikiásis aftokiníton*). See also DRIVING IN GREECE. It's not cheap to hire a car in Greece, and petrol, among the world's most expensive, adds heavily to the cost. Bargaining is sometimes possible with local firms.

Deposits are often waived for credit card holders and members of large tour groups who may also obtain a small discount. Though the International Driving Licence is legally obligatory for almost all foreign motorists (Britons are an exception), firms in practice accept virtually any national licence, stipulating that it must have been held for at least one year. A firm may well insist that the driver be 25.

**106**

Third-party liability insurance is often included in the rate, and complete coverage is available for a modest extra charge. All rates are subject to an 18% stamp duty and local taxes.

| | |
|---|---|
| I'd like to rent a car (tomorrow). | **Tha íthela na nikiáso éna afto-kínito (ávrio).** |
| For one day/a week | **giá mía iméra/mía evdomáda** |
| Please include full insurance. | **Sas parakaló na simberilávete miktí asfália.** |

## CIGARETTES, CIGARS, TOBACCO* *(tsigára; poúra; Kapnós).* The

sign to look for is ΚΑΠΝΟΠΩΛΕΙΟ—*kapnopolío* (tobacconist). Greek tobacco, most of it coming from Macedonia, is world-famous, and provided you stick to local products you'll find that smoking is a bargain in Greece. Local cigarettes range from very strong, unfiltered varieties to quite mild, filtered brands. *Astor* and *Old Navy* are popular, as is the menthol-flavoured *Mistral.* Most leading foreign cigarettes are available, but at two to three times the price of local brands. Dutch and Cuban cigars can also be purchased.

| | |
|---|---|
| A packet of …/A box of matches, please. | **Éna pakéto …/Éna koutí spírta, parakaló.** |
| filter-tipped/without filter | **me/chorís fíltro** |
| light/dark tobacco | **xanthós/mávros kapnós** |

## CITY TRANSPORT

**Bus Services***. Bus stops are recognized by the sign ΣΤΑΣΙΣ *(stásis).* There's a fairly good city bus network, but at rush hours, vehicles are very crowded, and, in summer, uncomfortably hot. Service throughout the city is provided from 5 a.m. to 1 a.m. A bus link between Athens (Sýntagma) and Piraeus runs 24 hours a day. Municipal buses for nearby swimming areas (Glifáda, Vouliagméni) along the Soúnion coast road leave regularly from Leofóros Ólgas, just by the entrance to the Temple of the Olympian Zeus.

You enter most buses by the rear (where conductors issue tickets); leave through the front door, and keep your ticket until the end of the journey as an inspector might come aboard.

**Taxi*** (ΤΑΞΙ—*taxi*). Taxis are all metered. There's an extra charge from the airport, the main bus terminals, ports and the railway stations. Night rates go into effect at midnight and last until 7 a.m.: **107**

there's an additional fee not shown on the meter. Past the city limits, the meter ticks over twice as fast, From Athens/Piraeus to Ekáli, Pérama, Elefsína. Várkiza and Agía Paraskeví, however, the normal tariff applies. If the occasion presents itself, taxi drivers prefer to take two or three different parties at the same time, each paying full fare.

Although taxi ranks exist, you're better off getting the hotel porter to hail a taxi for you or doing it yourself.

Tip: 10% is customary.

**Underground*** (ΗΛΕΚΤΡΙΚΟΣ—*ilektrikós*). Athens has a 20-stop underground (subway) system, operating between 5 and 12.45 a.m., but most of it actually runs above ground level. It connects the centre of Athens with Piraeus to the south and Kifisiá, a residential suburb, to the north. There are two fares, depending on distance. It's a good, fast, economical way to go, providing you avoid the rush hours. You must ask for your station by name when purchasing a ticket. Keep it until the end of your journey because you'll be asked for it at the exit.

| | |
|---|---|
| Where's the nearest underground station? | **Pou íne o kodinóteros stathmós tou ilektrikoú?** |
| What's the fare to …? | **Piá íne i timí giá …?** |
| When's the next bus to …? | **Póte févgi to epómeno leoforío giá …?** |

**CLOTHING.** Because of its Mediterranean climate, Athens tends to be informal; but, as in every large city, the people dress appropriately for the occasion. During business hours, you'll see just as many suits, shirts and ties and city dresses as you would in more temperate climes.

From the middle of May until the end of September, Athens is hot. Pack light clothing: drip-dry garments are the most practical. Bring a pair of good sunglasses.

Winter can mean decidedly chilly and wet weather, so don't forget at least a warm jacket or coat.

In spring and autumn, the evenings often turn cool. Light sweaters and cardigans, as well as a raincoat, are recommended.

Whether you're covering miles in museums or clambering around the Acropolis, lightweight rubber-soled shoes are a must.

## COMMUNICATIONS

**Post Office** (ΤΑΧΥΔΡΟΜΕΙΟ—*tachidromío*). Athens' central post office at Eólou 100 is open weekdays from 7.30 a.m. to 8 p.m. for poste restante (general delivery), registered letters and money orders, and until 9 p.m. for stamps from Monday to Saturday. The Sýntagma branch has the same hours. Other branch post offices tend to follow normal business hours.

The post office clerk is obliged to check the contents of any registered letters as well as of parcels addressed to foreign destinations, so don't seal this kind of mail until it has been "approved".

Stamps can also be purchased at news-stands and souvenir shops, but at a 10% surcharge. Letter boxes are painted yellow.

**Mail.** If you don't know ahead of time where you'll be staying, the central post office at Eólou 100 has a poste restante (general delivery) service (see above). Mail addressed to a specific district-branch post office in Athens can be picked up there on weekdays during business hours, with the exception of the Sýntagma branch. Take your passport along. Have your mail addressed to you in care of:

> Poste Restante
> Athens
> Greece

**Telegrams and Telephone** *(tilegráfima; tiléfono).* The Greek Telecommunications Organization's (OTE) head office at Patision 85 provides 24-hour service. Branch offices are open from 7 a.m. to 10 or 12 p.m.

Public telephone booths are scattered around the centre of Athens. Blue ones are for local calls only, while yellow ones permit direct dialling to other towns in Greece and to countries abroad connected to the international network. You'll find directions for use clearly written in English. OTE offices provide full service for all telex and telegram requirements.

| | |
|---|---|
| Where's the (nearest) post office? | **Pou íne to kodinótero tachidromío?** |
| Have you received any mail for …? | **Échete grámmata giá …?** |
| A stamp for this letter/ postcard, please | **Éna grammatósimo giaftó to grámma/kart postál, parakaló.** |
| express (special delivery) | **exprés** |
| airmail | **aeroporikós** |
| registered | **sistiméno** |
| I want to send a telegram to … | **Thélo na stílo éna tilegráfima sto …** |
| Can you get me this number in …? | **Boríte na mou párete aftó ton arithmó …?** |
| reverse-charge (collect) call | **plirotéo apó to paralípti** |
| person-to person (personal) call | **prosopikí klísi** |

**C** **COMPLAINTS.** Your hotel manager, the proprietor of the establishment in question or your travel-agency representative should be your first recourse if you have a complaint to make. If you obtain no satisfaction here, the tourist police (see POLICE) will be very interested to hear about anything you feel is wrong. All hotels and public places of amusement are price-controlled by the government. If it can be proved that you have been overcharged, you may be sure that the matter will be settled quickly.

**CONSULATES and EMBASSIES** *(proxenío; presvía).* Embassies of all major countries are located in Athens. However, as a foreign tourist with problems, you'll want to contact your consular representative, not your embassy—though they may often be found in the same building. Hours vary so it's best to call first.

**Australia:** Leofóros Mesogíon 15; tel.: 3604-611/15.
**Canada:** Gennadíou 4/Ipsilántou; tel.: 739-511.
**Great Britain***: Ploutárchou 1/Ipsilántou; tel.: 736-211.
**New Zealand:** Leofóros Vas. Sofías 29; tel.: 727-514.
**South Africa:** Leofóros Vas. Sofías 69; tel.: 729-050.
**U.S.A.:** Leofóros Vas. Sofías 91; tel.: 712-951.

**CONVERTER CHARTS.** For fluid and distance measures, see page 112. Greece uses the metric system.

**Temperature**

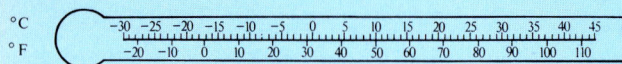

**Length**

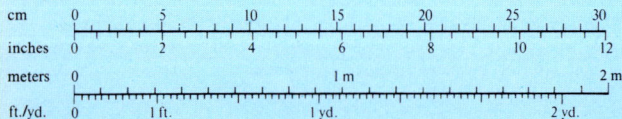

**Weight**

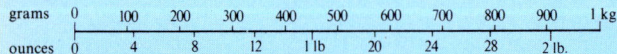

* Also for citizens of Eire.

**COURTESIES.** Greek hospitality is sincere, incredibly generous, sometimes overwhelming. Whatever you do, don't turn your back on it.

Because Athens is a big city, it's obviously prone to many of the same frustrations of city life that you could find in London or New York. If things get hot and uncomfortable on a bus journey, try to grin and bear it.

Greeks, in common with most Continental Europeans, wish each other "bon appetit" before starting a meal. In Greek, the expression is *kali órexi!* A common toast when drinking is *stin igiá sas!* meaning "cheers!". A reply to any toast, in the sense of "the same to you" is *epísis.*

The simple courtesies mean a lot in Greece and not only win friends but smooth your own way. It's a good idea and a simple matter to learn a few basic expressions, like please and thank you. See section on LANGUAGE.

**CRIME and THEFT.** Honesty is a matter of pride. Any idea of stealing from a guest is thoroughly repellent in this hospitable nation. Nevertheless, common sense suggests you keep an eye on things and confide valuable jewellery to the hotel reception.

You should keep in mind that possession of narcotics is a serious matter in Greece.

I want to report a theft.          **Thélo na katangílo mía klopí.**

## DRIVING IN GREECE

**Entering Greece:** To bring your car into Greece you'll need:

| International Driving Licence (see below) | car registration papers | Green Card (an extension to your regular insurance policy, making it valid for foreign countries) |
|---|---|---|
| | nationality plate or sticker | |

Normally, you're allowed to drive your car in Greece for up to four months. An international driving licence (not required for holders of a British licence) can be obtained through your home motoring association.

The standard European red warning triangle is required in Greece for emergencies. Seat belts are obligatory. Motorcycle drivers and their passengers must wear crash helmets.

**D**

Drive on the right and pass on the left. The Greeks have a bad habit of not always returning to the near-side lane, and of passing on right or left indiscriminately. Don't be afraid to use your horn, although, in theory, horn blowing is forbidden in town centres.

The motorways (expressways)—speed limit: 100 kilometres per hour—are good. Tolls are charged according to distance. Secondary roads are not so good. Main dangers lie in poor grading, wandering livestock (donkeys, goats and flocks of sheep) and bumps. Use care and always keep to the right.

**Driving conditions in Athens:** Traffic in Athens (speed limit: 50 kilometres per hour) is disciplined and has been considerably speeded up by the introduction of a one-way street system. Drivers are advised to stay alert at all times and watch for the changing of traffic lights. Greek drivers expect immediate reactions and tend to become impatient if they aren't forthcoming.

**Parking:** As in every other large city, there's a parking problem in Athens. Some hotels have built-in garages (which are expensive). Here are some principal parking areas mainly for foreign cars: Tosítsa, Deligiánni, Halkokondíli, Sína, Platía Mítropóleos, Platía Kotziá, Xenofóntos, Platía Koumountoúrou, Leofóros Ólgas, Áreos.

**Fuel and oil:** Petrol (gasoline) prices are among the highest in Europe.

**Fluid measures**

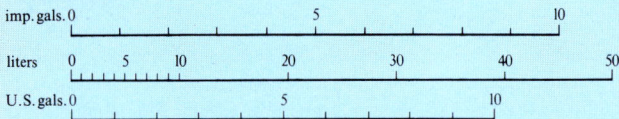

| imp. gals. | 0 | | 5 | | 10 |
|---|---|---|---|---|---|
| liters | 0 | 5 10 | 20 | 30 | 40 | 50 |
| U.S. gals. | 0 | | 5 | | 10 |

**Distance**

| km | 0 | 1 | 2 | 3 | 4 | 5 | 6 | 8 | 10 | 12 | 14 | 16 |
|---|---|---|---|---|---|---|---|---|---|---|---|---|
| miles | 0 | ½ | 1 | 1½ | 2 | 3 | 4 | 5 | 6 | 7 | 8 | 9 | 10 |

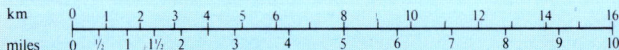

**Breakdowns:** Breakdown assitance is offered by the Automobile Association of Greece (ELPA) whose patrol network covers all the main highways of the mainland. Their vehicles bear the sign: "O.V.E.L.P.A."/"Assistance Routière A.T.C.C."/"Road Assistance". Telephone 104 for on-the-spot help.

ELPA's headquarters in Athens is located at Leofóros Mesogíon 2 (tel.: 7791-615).

**Road signs:** Most road signs are the standard pictographs used throughout Europe. However, you may encounter the following written signs in Greece:

| | |
|---|---|
| ΑΔΙΕΞΟΔΟΣ | No through road |
| ΑΛΤ | Stop |
| ΑΝΩΜΑΛΙΑ ΟΔΟΣΤΡΩΜΑΤΟΣ | Bad road surface |
| ΑΠΑΓΟΡΕΥΕΤΑΙ Η ΑΝΑΜΟΝΗ | No waiting |
| ΑΠΑΓΟΡΕΥΕΤΑΙ Η ΕΙΣΟΔΟΣ | No entry |
| ΑΠΑΓΟΡΕΥΕΤΑΙ Η ΣΤΑΘΜΕΥΣΙΣ | No parking |
| ΔΙΑΒΑΣΙΣ ΠΕΖΩΝ | Pedestrian crossing |
| ΕΛΑΤΤΩΣΑΤΕ ΤΑΧΥΤΗΤΑΝ | Reduce speed |
| ΕΠΙΚΙΝΔΥΝΟΣ ΚΑΤΩΦΕΡΕΙΑ | Dangerous incline |
| ΕΡΓΑ ΕΠΙ ΤΗΣ ΟΔΟΥ | Roadworks in progress (Men working) |
| ΚΙΝΔΥΝΟΣ | Caution |
| ΜΟΝΟΔΡΟΜΟΣ | One-way traffic |
| ΠΑΡΑΚΑΜΠΤΗΡΙΟΣ | Diversion (Detour) |
| ΠΟΔΗΛΑΤΑΙ | Cyclists |
| ΠΟΡΕΙΑ ΥΠΟΧΡΕΩΤΙΚΗ ΔΕΞΙΑ | Keep right |

| | |
|---|---|
| (International) Driving Licence | **(diethnís) ádia odigíseos** |
| car registration papers | **ádia kikloforías** |
| Green Card | **asfália aftokinítou** |
| Are we on the right road for …? | **Ímaste sto sostó drómo giá …?** |
| Full tank, please— | **Na to gemísete me venzíni** |
| normal/super. | **aplí/soúper, parakaló.** |
| Check the oil/tires/battery. | **Na elénxete ta ládia/ta lásticha/ ti bataría.** |
| I've had a breakdown. | **Épatha mía vlávi.** |
| There's been an accident. | **Égine éna distíchima.** |

**ELECTRIC CURRENT.** Athens has 220-volt, 50-cycle A.C. current. Sockets are either two- or three-pin. Larger hotels are often able to supply plug adaptors.

| | |
|---|---|
| an adaptor/a battery | **énas metaschimatistís/mía bataría** |

**EMERGENCIES.** See also CONSULATES and MEDICAL CARE. It's unlikely that you'll be anywhere in Athens where you won't find **113**

someone who speaks some English to help in an emergency. But if you're on your own and near a phone, here are some key numbers:

| | |
|---|---|
| Tourist Police | 171 |
| Police emergency squad | 100 |
| First aid (Red Cross) | 150 |
| Fire | 199 |
| Road assistance (Automobile Association) | 104 |

Though we hope you'll never need them, here are a few words you might want to learn in advance:

| | |
|---|---|
| Fire | **Fotiá** |
| Help | **Voíthia** |
| Police | **Astinomía** |
| Stop | **Stamatíste** |

**ENTRY and CUSTOMS REGULATIONS.** See also DRIVING. Most visitors, including British, American, Canadian, Irish, Australian. New Zealand and South African, need only a valid passport to enter Greece. British subjects are also admitted with a simplified Visitor's Passport. European and North American residents are not subject to any health requirements. In case of doubt, check with Greek representatives in your own country before departure.

The following chart shows what main duty-free items you may take into Greece and, upon your return home, into your own country:

| Into: | Cigarettes | | Cigars | | Tobacco | Spirits | | Wine |
|---|---|---|---|---|---|---|---|---|
| Greece | 200 | or 50 | | or | 200 g. | 1 bottle | | |
| Australia | 200 | or 250 g. | or | 250 g. | | 1 l. | or | 1 l. |
| Canada | 200 | and 50 | and | 900 | | 1.1 l. | or | 1.1 l. |
| Eire | 200 | or 50 | or | 250 g. | | 1 l. | and | 2 l. |
| N. Zealand | 200 | or 50 | or | ½ lb. | | 1 qt. | and | 1 qt. |
| S. Africa | 400 | and 50 | and | 250 g. | | 1 l. | and | 1 l. |
| U.K. | 200 | or 50 | or | 250 g. | | 1 l. | and | 2 l. |
| U.S.A. | 200 | and 100 | and | * | | 1 l. | or | 1 l. |

* a reasonable quantity

In addition to personal clothing, you may take into Greece a camera and a reasonable amount of film, a pair of binoculars, a typewriter, a radio, a tape recorder, musical instruments and sports equipment. In principle, these items are supposed to be declared when you enter the country, but in practice the authorities are very unlikely to bother you about them.

**Currency restrictions:** Foreign visitors to Greece are not allowed to take into or out of the country more than 1,500 drachmas in local currency. There is no limit on the foreign currency or traveller's cheques you may import or export as a tourist, though amounts in excess of $500 or its equivalent should be declared to the customs official upon arrival so you can take them out when you leave.

| | |
|---|---|
| I've nothing to declare. | **Den écho no dilóso típota.** |
| It's for my personal use. | **Íne giá prosopikí chrísi.** |

**GUIDES and INTERPRETERS*** *(xenagós; dierminéas).* Bilingual, licensed guides to all the museums and sites are available through the guides' association:

Somateíon Xenagón, Voulís 31; tel.: 3229-705.

It's a good idea to avoid 'freelance" guides encountered on sites.

For more serious problems, where you need an interpreter, contact your consulate.

| | |
|---|---|
| We'd like an English-speaking guide. | **Tha thélame éna xenagó na milá i angliká.** |
| I need an English interpreter. | **Chriázome éna ánglo dierminéa.** |

**HAIRDRESSERS *** (ΚΟΜΜΩΤΗΡΙΟ—*kommotírio*); **BARBERS** (ΚΟΥ-PEIO —*kourío*). You'll find women's hairdressers and barbers in the centre of town or in large hotels. For tipping suggestions, see TIPPING. Following are some phrases which might be useful:

| | |
|---|---|
| I'd like a shampoo and set. | **Thélo loúsimo ke miz-an-plí.** |
| I want a … | **Thélo …** |
| haircut | **koúrema** |
| blow-dry | **chténisma me to pistoláki** |
| colour chart | **éna digmatológio** |
| colour rinse | **mía deklorasión** |
| manicure | **manikioúr** |
| Don't cut it too short. | **Mi ta kópsete kondá.** |
| A little more off (here). | **Lígo pió kondá (edó).** |

115

**H** **HITCH-HIKING** *(oto-stóp)*. Legal everywhere in Greece, hitch-hiking is successfully practised by young and old all over the country.

| | |
|---|---|
| Can you give me/us a lift to …? | **Boríte na me/mas páte méchri to …?** |

**HOTELS and ACCOMMODATION*** (ΞΕΝΟΔΟΧΕΙΟ—*xenodochío;* ΔΩΜΑΤΙΑ—*domátia*). See also CAMPING and YOUTH HOSTELS. In the Athens area alone there are more than 160 hotels and boarding houses, ranging from the super luxury class to modest rooms in private homes. Furnished apartments are also available. It's a good idea to book in advance. Those who arrive without reservations should contact the Greek Chamber of Hotels at the airport to find a room. A similar office is open until late at night in the National Tourist Organization's central information bureau at Karagiórgi Servías 2, just off Sýntagma; or you can call the tourist police: 171.

Prices are controlled according to a category list compiled by the National Tourist Organization. Note, however, that de luxe or luxury establishments are not listed. Rooms in private homes are let at usually negotiable rates and conditions.

| | |
|---|---|
| I'd like a single/double room. | **Tha íthela éna monó/dipló domátio.** |
| with bath/shower | **me bánio/dous** |
| What's the rate per night? | **Piá íne i timí giá mía níkta?** |

**L** **LANGUAGE.** See also ALPHABET and box on page 11. It's unlikely you'll have much of a language problem if you stay within accepted tourist areas. Everyone concerned with tourism speaks either English, French, German or Italian. The big difficulty arises with street signs within the city. Although the government has promised that all street signs will eventually be posted in the Roman as well as the Greek alphabet, this has only been done so far on a few main avenues. Outside Athens (at Piraeus, for instance) and at major junctions within the city, directional signs and place names are in both alphabets.

Here are some Greek expressions to help you along:

| | |
|---|---|
| Good morning | **kaliméra** |
| Good afternoon | **kalispéra** |
| Good night | **kaliníkta** |
| Please | **parakaló** |
| Thank you | **efcharistó** |
| Goodbye | **chérete** |

The Berlitz phrase book GREEK FOR TRAVELLERS covers practically all situations you're likely to encounter in your travels in Greece.

Do you speak English?                    **Miláte angliká?**

**LAUNDRY and DRY CLEANING** (ΠΛΥΝΤΗΡΙΟ—*plintírio*; ΚΑΘ-ΑΡΙΣΤΗΡΙΟ—*katharistírio*). Launderettes operate in the city. Some have ironing or pressing facilities. Outside Athens, this service is rarely found, even in major towns.

Where's the nearest laundry/         **Pou íne to kodinótero plintírio/**
dry cleaners?                                    **katharistírio?**
When will it be ready?                   **Póte tha íne étimo?**
I must have this for tomorrow        **Prépi na íne étimo áviro to proí.**
morning.

**LOST PROPERTY.** Greeks have a reputation for honesty; if you lose something you have a good chance of getting it back. The lost property office is at Leofóros Mesogíon 14 (tel.: 7705-711).

**Lost children.** Should your child wander off, immediately report it to the police emergency squad (tel.: 100) and then to the nearest police station. The tourist police aren't directly concerned with such matters, but will obviously help out on the language side.

I've lost my wallet/handbag/        **Échasa to portofóli mou/**
passport.                                         **ti tsánda mou/to diavatirió mou.**

**MAPS.** You'll find that some maps give names only in Greek, some use both Greek and Latin and others simply have Latin transliterations. Falk-Verlag which did the cartography for this book also publishes a comprehensive map covering the whole of Athens and surroundings.

a street plan of Athens                  **éna odikó chárti ton Athinón**
a road map of this region              **éna chárti aftís tis periochís**

**MEDICAL CARE.** See also EMERGENCIES. To be completely at your ease, take out health insurance to cover the risk of illness and accident while on holiday. Your travel agent or insurance company at home will be able to advise you.

There's an efficient network of hospitals and clinics in the Athens area. Your hotel receptionist will be able to find you a doctor who speaks English.

The municipal hospital (K.A.T.) at Leofóros Mesogíon (tel.: 7701-211) operates a 24-hour emergency clinic (tel.: 166).

**Pharmacies** (ΦAPMAKEIO—*farmakío*): A red or green cross on a white background identifies a *farmakío*. *Farmakía* take turns at remaining open during the siesta, at night and on Sundays. Your hotel, tour guide, the local English-language press or the tourist police will locate them. It's advisable to bring any special medication with you.

| | |
|---|---|
| Where's the nearest (all-night) pharmacy? | **Pou íne to kodinótero (dianikterévon) farmakío?** |
| a doctor/a dentist | **énas giatrós/énas odontogiatrós** |
| an ambulance | **éna asthenofóro** |
| hospital | **nosokomío** |
| an upset stomach | **varistomachiá** |
| sunstroke | **ilíasi** |
| a fever | **piretós** |

**MEETING PEOPLE.** Despite its air of emancipation, customs in Athens are not so different from those of the countryside. Girls, though not actually escorted by brothers or parents, are still for the most part under relatively close parental control. Free to find employment, they may not be free to find a flat to share with a friend. A man, however, is a law unto himself—and may well press his charms though not his suit.

**MONEY MATTERS**

**Currency** *(nómisma).* Greece's monetary unit is the drachma (*drachmí* abbreviated drs.—in Greek, Δρχ.). One drachma is divided into 100 leptas *(leptá).* While there are still a few 10- and 20-lepta coins in circulation, you probably won't see anything smaller than the 50-leptá piece. Other coins are 1, 2, 5, 10 and 20 drachmas. Until recently, old and new series of coins were circulating at the same time; as of present, the old are gradually being withdrawn. There are banknotes of 50, 100, 500 and 1,000 drachmas.

**Banks and Currency-Exchange Offices** (TPAΠEZA—*trápeza;* ΣYN-AΛΛAΓMA—*sinállagma*). Banking hours vary but are normally 8 a.m. to 2.30 p.m. Monday to Thursday (Friday until 2 p.m.). However, some banks' foreign exchange bureaux remain open until 7 or 8 p.m. The Sýntagma branch of the National Bank of Greece is open continuously from 8 a.m. to 9 p.m. Monday to Friday, and from 8 a.m. to 8 p.m. on Saturdays, Sundays and public holidays. When changing money, always take your passport with you.

**Credit Cards and Traveller's Cheques** (*pistotikí kárta; "traveller's cheque"*). Internationally known credit cards are instantly recognized—at least by car-hire firms and those shops dealing with anything of substantial interest to the visitor. For dining out, you're better off relying on cash. All the major brands of traveller's cheques are readily accepted. Always take your passport for identification. Eurocheques are now accepted in many places.

| | |
|---|---|
| I want to change some pounds/ dollars. | **Thélo na alláxo merikés líres/ meriká dollária.** |
| Do you accept traveller's cheques? | **Pérnete "traveller's cheques"?** |
| Can I pay with this credit card? | **Boró na plieróso ma aftí ti pistotikí kárta?** |
| How much? | **Póso káni?** |
| Have you something cheaper? | **Échete káti ftinótero?** |

**MUSEUM HOURS.** Most museums open at 9 a.m. on weekdays, 10 on Sundays and holidays, and close anywhere from 2 to 7 p.m. depending on the season—later hours being in effect in the summer. Archaeological sites usually have somewhat longer hours. In any case, it's best to check the latest schedules on the spot.

All museums and sites close on January 1, March 25, Good Friday (until noon), Easter Sunday and Christmas and at midday on certain other holidays. The **Acropolis Museum, Agorá Museum, Benáki Museum** and **Delphi Museum** close on Tuesdays; the **National Archaeological Museum, Byzantine Museum** and **National Gallery of Painting** close on Mondays.

Archaeological sites are generally open seven days a week. The Agorá, however, closes on Tuesdays.

**NEWSPAPERS, MAGAZINES, BOOKS** (*efimerída; periodikó; vivlío*). Most European papers—including the British press and the Paris-based *International Herald Tribune*—appear on news-stands in the centre of town in the afternoon or evening of the day of publication. Two local English-language papers, the *Athens News* and the *Athens Post*, come out in the morning. A monthly magazine in English, *The Athenian*, has a comprehensive listing of restaurants, nightclubs, cinemas and theatres, and a directory of useful phone numbers. The National Tourist Organization issues *The Week in Athens*, free of charge.

Foreign-language book-shops, carrying all the latest in European publications. American and English paper-backs and travel maps, can be found on Níkis, just off Sýntagma, and on Amerikís, just off Eleftheríou Venizélou (otherwise known as Panepistimíou).

| | |
|---|---|
| Have you any English-language newspapers? | **Échete anglikés efimerídes?** |

**PHOTOGRAPHY.** A photo shop is advertised by the sign ΦΩΤΟΓΡΑ-ΦΕΙΟ *(fotografío)*. Major brands of colour and black-and-white film for still and cine-cameras are widely available, but prices are no bargains—it's probably best to buy film before your holiday and take it home for processing. Polaroid film is difficult to find.

Hand-held cameras may be used in most museums and on archaeological sites for a slight extra charge. For home-movie camera shots on sites, consult the General Department of Antiquities, Museum Section, Odós Aristídou 14.

| | |
|---|---|
| I'd like a roll of film for this camera. | **Tha íthela éna film giaftí ti michaní.** |
| black-and-white film | **asprómavro film** |
| colour prints | **énchromo film** |
| colour slides | **énchromo film giá sláïds** |
| 35-mm film | **éna film triánda pénde milimétr** |
| super-8 | **soúper-októ** |
| How long will it take to develop (and print) this film? | **Se póses iméres boríte na emfanísete (ke na ektipósete) aftó to film?** |
| May I take a picture? | **Boró na páro mía fotografía?** |

**POLICE** *(astinomía).* Athens has three types of police. The *touristikí astinomía* (tourist police) usually wear grey uniforms with flags on their jackets identifying the languages they speak. Aside from helping visitors personally, they accompany state inspectors to hotels and restaurants to ensure that proper standards and prices are maintained. If you have any complaint or want any information, phone 171 (on duty 24 hours a day), or go to Leofóros Singroú 7 (tel.: 9239-224).

The rural police operating outside the city boundaries, are called *chorofílakes.* They wear shoulder cordons with their green uniforms, and you'll see them in white helmets on motorcycles.

Finally, Athens has a separate municipal police force, *astinomía póleon;* its members have flashy white patrol cars but their uniforms change according to the season: in summer they are greyish green, in winter, green.

| | |
|---|---|
| Where's the nearest police station? | **Pou íne to kodinótero astinomikó tmíma?** |

**PUBLIC HOLIDAYS** *(argíes).* Banks, offices and shops are closed on the following national holidays:

| | | |
|---|---|---|
| Jan. 1 | *Protochroniá* | New Year's Day |
| Jan. 6 | *ton Theofaníon* | Epiphany |
| March 25 | *Ikostí Pémti Martíou (tou Evangelismoú)* | Greek Independence Day |
| May 1 | *Protomagiá* | May Day |
| Aug. 15 | *Dekapendávgoustos (tis Panagías)* | Assumption Day |
| Oct. 28 | *Ikostí Ogdóï Oktovríou* | *Óchi* ("No") Day, commemorating Greek defiance of Italian ultimatum and invasion of 1940 |
| Dec. 25 | *Christoúgenna* | Christmas Day |
| Dec. 26 | *défteri iméra ton Christougénnon* | St. Stephen's Day |
| Movable dates: | *Katharí Deftéra* | 1st Day of Lent: Clean Monday |
| | *Megáli Paraskeví* | Good Friday |
| | *Deftéra tou Páscha* | Easter Monday |
| | *Análipsis* | Ascension |

In addition to these nation-wide holidays, Athens celebrates its patron saint's day—*tou Agíou Dionisíou* (St. Dionysios the Areopagite) on October 3—as a legal holiday.

*Note:* The dates on which the movable holy days are celebrated often differ from those in Catholic and Protestant countries.

| | |
|---|---|
| Are you open tomorrow? | **Échete aniktá ávrio?** |

**R** **RADIO and TV** *(rádio; tileórasi)*. The Greek National Radio (ERT) broadcasts the news and weather in English early in the morning. For transmission times, consult the local English-language newspapers.

On short-wave bands, reception of the World Service of the BBC is extremely clear. Voice of America's English programmes are also easily picked up.

Most hotels, and some bars and restaurants have TV lounges. Many of the programmes are imported English TV series with Greek subtitles.

**RELIGIOUS SERVICES.** The national church is the Greek Orthodox. Visitors of certain other faiths will be able to attend services at the following places:

**Catholic:** St. Denis, Venizélou 24; tel.: 3623-603. Masses in Latin.

**Protestant:** St. Paul's (Anglican) Filellínon 29; tel.: 714-906. Services in English.
St. Andrew's Protestant American Church, Sína 66; tel.: 7707-448. Services in English.

**Jewish:** Beth Shalom Synagogue, Melidóni 6; tel.: 3252-823. Services in English.

**S** **SIESTA.** Notwithstanding the country's entry into the Common Market, the midday pause remains a hallowed tradition in Greece. Most shops and businesses close up and Athens shifts into low gear between 2.30 and 5 p.m.

**T** **TIME DIFFERENCES.** The chart below shows the time difference between Greece and various cities in winter. In summer, Greek clocks are put forward one hour.

|          | New York | London   | **Athens** | Jo'burg | Sydney | Auckland |
|----------|----------|----------|------------|---------|--------|----------|
| winter:  | 5 a.m.   | 10 a.m.  | **noon**   | noon    | 9 p.m. | 11 p.m.  |
| summer:  | 5 a.m.   | 10 a.m.  | **noon**   | 11 a.m. | 7 p.m. | 9 p.m.   |

What time is it?                                    **Ti óra íne?**

**TIPPING.** By law, service charges are included in the bill at hotels, restaurants and *tavérnes*. The Greeks aren't tip-crazy, but they do expect you to leave a little more—if the service has been good, of course.

**122**

Even if your room or meals are included as part of a package tour, you'll still want to remember the maid and the waiter. The waiter will probably have a *mikró* (an assistant, or busboy), who should get a token of appreciation as well.

| | |
|---|---|
| Hotel porter, per bag | 20–30 drs. |
| Maid, per day | 25–30 drs. |
| Waiter | 5% (optional) |
| Taxi driver | 10% |
| Tourist guide (½ day) | 50–80 drs. |
| Hairdresser | 10% |
| Theatre usher | 10–20 drs. (optional) |
| Lavatory attendant | 10 drs. |

**TOILETS** (ΤΟΥΑΛΕΤΤΕΣ—*toualéttes*). Public toilets are located in parks and squares throughout the centre of town. If there's someone in attendance, you should leave a small tip. In cafés, if you drop in specifically to use the facilities, it's customary to have a coffee or some other drink before leaving. Except in modest establishments, there are generally two doors, marked ΓΥΝΑΙΚΩΝ (ladies) and ΑΝΔΡΩΝ (gentlemen).

**TOURIST INFORMATION OFFICES** (*grafío plироforión tourismoú*). The National Tourist Organization staff will do all they can to aid you, both in preparing for your trip and while you're in Greece. They supply a wide range of accurate, colourful brochures and maps for the region in various languages and can give information on hotel prices and addresses, campsites and itineraries.

**Australia.** 51–57 Pitt St., Sydney, N.S.W. 2000; tel. (02) 241-1663.

**British Isles.** 195–7, Regent St., London W1R 8DL; tel. (01) 734-5997.

**Canada.** 2, place Ville Marie, Suite 67, Esso Plaza, Montreal, Que., H3B 2C9; tel. (514) 871-1535.

**South Africa.** 108 Fox St., Johannesburg; tel. (836) 834-2551.

**U.S.A.** 645 5th Ave., New York, NY 10022; tel. (212) 421-5777;
627 W. 6th St., Los Angeles, CA 90017; tel. (213) 626-6696;
168 N. Michigan, Ave., Chicago, IL 60601; tel. (312) 782-1084.

**T**  The central headquarters of the National Tourist Organization (*Ellini-kós Organismós Tourismoú*, abbreviated EOT) in Athens is located at Amerikís 2 (tel.: 3223-111/9).

The main information office is inside the National Bank at Karagiórgi Servías 2, just off Sýntagma; tel.: 3222-545.

Hours: 8 a.m. to 2 p.m. and from 2.30 to 8 p.m., Monday to Friday, and from 8 a.m. to 2 p.m. on Saturdays.

There's also an office at the airport (tel.: 9799-500).

Where's the tourist office?   **Pou íne to grafío tourismoú?**

**TRAINS.** The Greek National Railways (OSE) provides a convenient local service to the Peloponnese (Mycenae, Árgos, Trípolis, Patras, for example) from Peloponnese Station (Stathmós Peloponnísou). A fast connection to Thessaloníki (Salonica) leaves from the major international station, Stathmós Larísis.

Single (one-way) tickets are valid for the day of issue only and for a particular, specified train. Return (round-trip) tickets are good for a month. Sleeping accommodation can be arranged through the Wagon-Lits offices at Karagiórgi Servías 2; tel.: 3242-281/8. Ordinary first-and second-class tickets are sold at all railway stations and travel agencies. Always book in advance; trains are sometimes very crowded.

When's the next train to …?   **Póte févgi to epómeno tréno giá …?**

single (one-way)   **apló**
return (round-trip)   **me epistrofí**

**Y**  **YOUTH HOSTELS** (ΞΕΝΩΝ ΝΕΟΤΗΤΟΣ—*xenón neótitos*). If you're a member of the International Youth Hostels Association, you'll be eligible to stay at any of the three hostels in Athens or the one in Piraeus. Otherwise, you can ask for an International Guest Card at the Greek Youth Hostels Headquarters:

Dragatsaníou 4 (7th floor), off Platía Klafthmónos.

Information and addresses can be obtained from the National Tourist Organization office at Sýntagma.

Also providing inexpensive accommodation are the YMCA (**XAN**) at Omírou 28 (tel.: 3626-970) and the YWCA (**XEN**) at Amerikís 11 **124** (tel.: 3624-291), both open throughout the year.

**WATER** *(neró)*. Athens' tap water is perfectly safe to drink. Bottled mineral water, usually still rather than fizzy, is always available (ask for *Loutráki*).

| a bottle of mineral water | **éna boukáli metallikó neró** |
|---|---|
| fizzy (carbonated) | **me anthrakikó** |
| still | **chorís anthrakikó** |

---

## SOME USEFUL EXPRESSIONS

| yes/no | **ne/óchi** |
|---|---|
| please/thank you | **parakaló/efcharistó** |
| excuse me/you're welcome | **me sinchoríte/típota** |

| where/when/how | **pou/póte/pos** |
|---|---|
| how long/how far | **póso keró/póso makriá** |
| yesterday/today/tomorrow | **chthes/símera/ávrio** |
| day/week/month/year | **iméra/evdomáda/mínas/chrónos** |

| left/right | **aristerá/dexiá** |
|---|---|
| up/down | **epáno/káto** |
| good/bad | **kalós/kakós** |
| big/small | **megálos/mikrós** |
| cheap/expensive | **ftinós/akrivós** |

| hot/cold | **zestós/kríos** |
|---|---|
| old/new | **paliós/néos** |
| open/closed | **aniktós/klistós** |

| Does anyone here speak English? | **Milá kanís anglicá?** |
|---|---|
| I don't understand. | **Den katalavéno.** |
| Please write it down. | **Parakaló grápste to.** |
| What does this mean? | **Ti siméni aftó?** |
| How much is that? | **Póso káni aftó?** |
| I'd like … | **Tha íthela …** |
| Where are the toilets? | **Pou íne i toaléttes?** |
| Waiter! | **Garçon, parakaló!** |
| Can you help me, please? | **Voïthíste me, parakaló.** |
| Call a doctor—quickly! | **Kaléste éna giatró—grígora!** |

# Index

An asterisk (*) next to a page number indicates a map reference. For index to Practical Information, see p. 103.

126